# Whomba WaR

# Whomba War

Paul Marion Geiger

# Whomba War
## Copyright © 2014 by Paul Marion Geiger

ISBN 978-0-578-91285-1

This book is dedicated to Alan, Frank, Gary, Gooch, John, Mark, Michael, Rose Ann, Sal, Thomas, and Wayne. Also, to all who lived the life of the 60's and endured the scars from the Wars here at home.

# Chapter 1: Nineteen Sixty-Eight

Everyone I have ever had the pleasure, and maybe some not the pleasure, to meet has told me our government only releases certain highly secretive materials fifty years after the fact.

These delayed disclosures are mostly of the embarrassing kind or of a somewhat unlawful nature. Either reason; they are usually held back for public safety and government privacy policies. That being the case, I now believe I have waited long enough in my suppression of the facts related to the Whomba War.

At the time of my typing the very first word at the top of this page it is five months and four years shy of the fifty year anniversary. I'm starting now with the understanding that by the time I have it all down in black and white the vital date will surely have passed.

Just as in the case of all recollections from forty-six years in the past; sometimes there is another person's view on the topic. I'm affirming here and now, for the record, that if any other view were to be inspected from top to bottom one would have to admit; "These stories are carbon copies; duplicates."

Why would I have the nerve to have an opinion so bold as this; when the story hasn't even begun to be written? Simple.

Back then we, all the names that will follow, lived together as one family of kids in the neighborhood. For each summer when we were off from school we shared each other's time, possessions, families and thoughts.

The summer of Nineteen Sixty-Eight was as different a time compared to today, as if we tried to compare last week with the first week after man invented fire or the wheel.

We didn't lock ourselves in our rooms with a smart phone or stay up all hours of the night entertaining ourselves on the internet. We slept at night in the Sixties.

Hell; we were tired from our nonstop days. Everyone back then lived. They mostly didn't have a huge choice on how they lived, but they lived all the same.

When you heard about one of the guys being indoors it was taken for granted he was either being punished for some wrongdoing or about to die. People didn't stay in the house in their off time. There was a world waiting for them beyond that front door. A world that could disappear in a heartbeat if either the U. S. or Russian leaders thought it should.

Strange how people really start to appreciate something when there is a fear it may vanish forever. Today we donate hard cash and pray for the survival of the Polar Bear and the elephant. When I was fourteen years old we thought about a bigger issue; the planet.

I may be wrong, I was only fourteen back then, but I don't remember any television commercials or ads in magazines for donating to save the planet. I guess they figured if we were supposed to go door to door with one of those UNICEF boxes we'd need something more the size of a boxcar.

Or maybe it was more simple than that. Maybe when everyone knew of somebody's father, brother, cousin, uncle or classmate getting killed or maimed over in Nam they just didn't care about anything outside the family.

Maybe the grownups at the time ran out of tears and compassion. Maybe that's why they took so long to stop our side from killing those other people over in that God forsaken jungle.

We were told back then that they didn't think and act the way they should. Hell; they didn't even look like us. How can you trust a people that don't look like us? So I, like every child that matures, learned later that we're not always on the team with the highest moral values. But our team always won; so we were told.

Growing up in the Sixties was a time where everyone around you was familiar with war. It was as commonplace as polio and TB. Your grandparents went through the First and Second World Wars. Some of them had even heard the stories of the great Civil War from their grandparents firsthand.

Your own parents went through the Second World War or if not that at least the Korean War. Even if you were one of the lucky one in two-hundred million that didn't have a relative die in Vietnam, Laos or Cambodia; you'd still be exposed to the misery at school, work or place of worship.

So it was different back then. The kids in high school and college paid attention to the political leaders at the time in a different sort of way. They didn't care how eloquent the person spoke or how good they looked in a suit. Their judgment was more on a personal note.

Was the next senator, congressman or president going to be in a pissing match with some other world leader? Was the next guy voted into the capital building going to be putting his money in the U. S. timber industry because he knows caskets will be selling by the thousands?

The social security crowd of today hesitates to look back on what those days were really like. They've forgotten something very vital they had learned in school; history does repeat itself.

Now when you hear a senior citizen complain about the government it revolves around what they haven't got in the way of money or benefits. If reminded, more than half would tell you at age twenty-one they voted more to save the countries young men from senseless death overseas, than a one percent COLA.

Seems they cared more back then about a friend in school; than they do now about their own child or grandchild when it comes to voting out the war-monger.

Unlike most of the sixty-plus year olds walking the streets today; I try to force myself to remember the Sixties at least once a month. I try to think back on the time when money wasn't so abundant and yet we got by. When modern medicine wasn't able to conquer a heart attack or cancer as it does today. When we kids didn't stare or make fun of men with no arms and legs; a small by-product of war. When the only eighteen year-old who didn't worry about dying in a foreign land was a retard.

Actually, I've noticed there seems to be a lot more younger men today with missing limbs. They aren't so recognizable until you go to the beach where the artificials become a nuisance. I have the highest respect for these guys. I'm not ashamed to say that as soon as I get myself to a private location I usually wipe the tear from my eye.

Funny isn't it? When I was a kid you'd always see the older men crying at the Memorial Day parade. Took my stupid ass over fifty years to finally understand why.

There is always a difference in the past and the present. Back then I think they were crying for their friends that sacrificed "ALL" for their love of country. Today I have to admit I cry because I believe it is our country that has sacrificed our men for certain politician's "ALL".

My grandfather told me as a young boy that you couldn't start a war without a politician and a manufacturer of weapons.

When I asked, "What about the soldier? The soldier does all the fighting."

He didn't make a smile. No, he was as serious as could be, "My boy, the soldier is always in the middle. The politician will start and end the fight. But it's always the soldier who's in the middle of it. Ever hear of a politician coming home in a B-Bag? Hasn't happened when I was your age and it sure as shit won't happen when you're mine."

I'm getting pretty close to that age he spoke of and I think he may have been on to something back then.

To put it in perspective if you like; in a nutshell. The Sixties were a time when every ethnic, religious and age group seemed to be at each other's throat.

Though there was one common thread that bound the Jew to the Episcopalian, the Black to the White, the young to the old, and the rich to the poor. And this slim strand of the media, called the evening news, was starting to fray like the fringes of the flag that flew over Ft. McHenry.

Money, power, education and sheer stupidity could no longer shield one's own true conscience as to the reality of what was going on outside; past the La-Z-Boy tucked in the corner by the Zenith.

Men on all channels, from ABC to PIX, started to share their own personal doubts out loud. The politeness of keeping quiet and following in the steps of the views of Government Almighty was being questioned. An American society based on something other than war was being pondered.

History is always slow to move unless there is a revolution. We all know that we never had an uprising back then, so it took a while longer for the idea of a warless nation to be slowly indoctrinated into our society.

Granted it may have went a little smoother and faster had we not had so many great American heroes like Archie Bunker to put people like Walter Cronkite to rest. I always thought Archie would have liked it if King George had kept his colonies; he'd probably would have even "voted" for the man.

All I can say about the political view of a fourteen year-old in Sixty-Eight is; I was so grateful we hadn't outgrown our War Years.

I can't imagine how bored I would have been; fishing and playing baseball every afternoon with the guys who had just entered college.

I would have heard the older guys talking about girls and getting an education, instead of how to get to Canada on foot or how long it takes to bleed out from a punji.

I'd guarantee I'd never have had the chance to have the mind and know-how of a twenty year-old at the age of fourteen. You can't imagine how fast a person's mental acuity can grow listening to stories of monks setting themselves on fire and Air Force runs over foreign lands that drop bombs by the mega-ton. It was much better listening to the guys hanging around the school grounds, than Ben Cartwright bitching at Hop Sing.

It was almost comforting at night to put your head down on a soft pillow knowing God was on your side. We were bombing someone, somewhere; as long as I can remember. And will be bombing someone, somewhere else; for the times to come.

It must have been a great feeling. I can't say I ever remember having that feeling at that age, but it must have been great. Otherwise; why did everyone support it with such pride and enthusiasm?

Yes, I was an American. Albeit; only fourteen years old. Still, even at that age, when the older guys wanted me to be on their side in the Whomba War; how could I refuse? Hell, I'm an American.

I was born right where the Manhattan Transit lines cross the infamous Garden State Parkway. Who could be more American than me? Sure, I was only fourteen.

If this was the American Revolution and the King's men had just hung my father and uncles the day before; was this no different? To be called for action in the Whomba War was to be called upon as a patriot. God was watching closely for my response. I agreed to serve with my fellow Americans; I agreed most religiously.

I do remember going to my Uncle Andy's bar in Passaic and hearing the old men talk about the First World War with a sheer horror in their voices. The stories of the mustard gas were gruesome.

Worse thing I remember about their discussions on the gas was how it destroyed the mind and soul of the soldier before it took his life. It forced them to make a choice. Not of whether to stay and fight or run and live. No, it wasn't that elementary. They had to choose how they preferred to succumb on the field of battle.

To escape the toxic effects of a gas, that was heavier than air and hugged the ground, many men would simply stand up. Of course; within three seconds of standing erect their heads would be blown off.

So as the men drank they would discuss the choices they had made back then in the trenches. Stay down on your stomach and get gassed or stand tall and get shot to hell.

I was always impressed that even after hours of drinking they never changed their original decisions. Thinking back

now, at those times in the bar, I'm aware they had fifty years
to rethink on their preferred selection. If time didn't sway
them, I guess alcohol couldn't either.

At the VFW and Legion the guys chain-smoked, drank
and talked about the freezing conditions in the Ardennes
and North Korea. A few would cough up a little blood from
the jungle diseases they caught in Burma or The Philippines.

The Vietnam Viet was non-existent. They hated to be in
the public eye. Probably because the simpleminded public
hated them for doing what they were forced to do.

The World War II generation was tired of the younger
generation's protest of war. They would prefer to have their
Commy sons shot, than enrolled in the local community
college. Always not comprehending why their own children
were too stupid to understand they were directed by the
ever-loved politicians. The ones their knowledgeable parents
elected and reelected.

Responsibility and consciousness have never been an
American strong suit. When the person they voted for does
exactly what he or she said they'd do and it hurts someone
else, the inept ass-wipe who voted for them will say; "Well, I
didn't hear that. Can that be true? Maybe you're wrong."

Obviously, they never hear any of the truth, cause some
of the people that were in power then are still in power
today.

The men in the war-clubs all talked about their particular
war. They hardly talked of work, finances, or even women.
The subject of the past, the now and the future would be of
our strength as a nation and upon which foreign land we

should use it upon. We were still praising the glory of World Wars I and II and somehow not the latter two conflicts.

Would the parade next May have men standing at attention for all to cheer those that fought the battle so close to home? Would the bars and armed forces clubs be speaking about the third major conflict since the one with Germany and Japan? Would it be Mr. Rooney or Mr. Cronkite who puts on his turtle shell and crawls among the weed covered hills searching for the truth? What news station would become the first to disclose to the world the true facts of the first war in Bergen County since General Washington's time?

The way to win a war is to be prepared and be secretive. All good generals and politicians alike know this. There were a few there at Gantner those nights before the encounter that would have made either an impressive general or a noble politician.

Proof of this is in the libraries or on the internet today. Try doing a search for the Whomba War and see what you get. Not a damn thing.

You want to talk about a well-kept secret military operation. And a War no less. Yes, I think you would agree with this fourteen year-old back in Nineteen Sixty-Eight.

# Chapter 2: Saturday

I awoke before my alarm went off; which was common for me. I went straight to the bathroom and after a quick shower started to dress for my job at the sub shop.

Putting my jeans on I felt my right back pocket being lighter than it should be. I didn't remember taking my wallet out the night before but checked the dresser anyway. Nothing. I really didn't think so. Gooch, my older brother, had struck again.

My time to start on Saturday was around ten. Leaving me plenty of time to run down to the river and turn the pump on for the farm's irrigation; if needed. As of yesterday the fields needed the water and as far as I knew it hadn't rained during the night.

Beets, radishes and scallions take a huge amount of water. I always wondered if the people eating at places like The Tavern on the Green and the Brass Rail at night were aware that many vegetables they ate were drinking from the Passaic that very morning. We all knew; we still ate the crops.

Under my socks, in the second drawer down, I kept a five hidden for days like this. My brother, Al Riley and Gary Riley were off at Greenwood Lake fishing for the day. The soonest I'd have my wallet, with my fishing license, would be around five or six.

Hopefully, it wouldn't be a repeat of last year, when my brother and the Gaglione kid swamped the row boat and lost everything, and I mean everything.

My brother was well aware of the fact I'd be working until six, so I assume he thought he'd be in the clear. A cousin owned the sub shop so getting lunch or any other meal wasn't really a problem. I know that twelve bucks is a lot for a fishing license, but common now. Hell, we went almost every day in the summer and weekends during the school year.

I walked down the farm road toward the river kicking the dirt every thirty to fifty feet. It was dry even though it had been watered the day before.

It was closer to ten than I thought; I could see the farmhands had already started on five separate rows. I would have been there in the field with them if it weren't Saturday; my day to work the sub shop. I worked the fields most days in the summer. During the school year when the farm lay idle I worked almost every night at the sandwich shop.

Walking into work I could still hear the sound of the pump, which was no more than fifty yards downstream. Today was going to comprise of slicing about ten cases of tomatoes and shredding six cases of Iceberg lettuce. We did this almost every day. Tomatoes can last a day or two. Lettuce on the other hand, once it's cut, has a lifespan of about six hours.

The place had one hell of a following. Mostly due to the freshness and quality of the ingredients. I learned at fourteen years old from working there you can make a shitload of "Lettuce" for yourself; if you treat the customer right.

I was home before six and back in the shower rinsing off the smell of tomatoes and deli meats. As if my morning was a dream, by the time I returned to my room, my wallet was back in my jeans. I checked the contents before putting one stitch of clothes on. The license and all my money were still intact; even dry. Of course my brother was nowhere in sight.

He and Gary were usually off to a bar in the next town over by eight. It was one of those old Polish bars that served the local older walk-ins and the slightly underage sneak-ins. Even I could get in on a real crowded night.

Anyone having a brother older than them can understand that my brother and I didn't get along most of the time. He hung around with Gary Riley and I often went places with Gary's older brother Al. They lived across the street and we've known each other all our lives.

Alan was three years and fifty days older than me, but I seemed more mature than either his brother or mine. We worked together in the fields and Sub Base; until he was old enough to get descent work.

His brother and my brother were like Siamese twins. They seemed to go everywhere together; except maybe work. I really can't remember what those two did all day. They never seemed to have a job. Not until they were around sixteen or seventeen. Must have been nice.

Saturday night meant one thing to a fourteen year old kid. Where were we, Al was now seventeen, going to get served tonight? That's right. Al looked like he was around nineteen; long hair and able to bullshit his way anywhere. I was as tall, if not taller, so people assumed if he was old enough; so was I.

We'd go into the City and hit places like the Jockey Club at the Tropicana. Years later my dad would stick his hand in a pocket of a sport coat I had borrowed and find almost twenty of those chips they'd give you for a five dollar admission.

I'd get a load of them when I opened my jacket and the bouncers would see a sewn in police badge. One of the few perks of being a "Cop's Kid".

My best friend Al had hair way down past his collar, while my brother and I were allowed one micron past our collars.

The War was now on full tilt and we'd always hear from our father. "What if the Governor or a Senator should see you? Do you want them to think you're a Hippy or Protester?"

We found out it wasn't that our father was "Pro-War"; he just wanted to keep his job. The Sixties were funny years like that. Any sign you were against the Government and you were out. No ifs, ands, or buts.

I often would ask Al why so many places let us in. We of course never went to a place in our own hometown, but anywhere in the City or ten miles away seemed easy pickings.

He would explain that with The War on and no guys around the young women had nobody to talk to and dance with. We were good looking and always well dressed; which got us in. He always tipped heavily and made sure we never drank more than two or three. No exceptions.

The ladies were always buying me those Singapore Slings, they were kind of sweet, but I drank them anyway. I could easily handle at least six. Of course I never told Al how many I'd really had.

We were never drunk in public or walking in our own backdoor. Unlike our brothers, the Garys, who at age sixteen already knew the backseat of a patrol car blindfolded.

Growing up in the age of war it wasn't a spectacular surprise that my brother and I fought like two of those Beta Fish. There were times I really could have done some damage if I wanted too.

I was taller and a whole lot stronger; he never did any kind of farm work. We did take karate classes at our uncle's studio in Kearney, but he didn't take that very serious either. He probably should have; maybe he'd at least won one fight.

With war the main subject of the Twentieth Century it was more of a miracle either one of us survived until the draft age. We seemed to fight constantly at that age. We were supposed to; after all we were Americans.

All the other kids on our street were Americans too and they acted like it. When I think of the biggest brawls Gooch and I had, they were miniscule in respect to some of the other brothers.

One instance that really stood out back then was the time Wayne D'Amico got so mad at his older brother Mark. Mark had the size and seventeen month advantage over Wayne and yet he still was having a hard time getting him to give up.

Wayne was just like that; he never knew when to stop. It was as if his body was taken over by a mad, rabid spirit.

Mark was standing behind the kitchen door ignoring his brother; even after Wayne's verbal attack kept escalating. Mark had realized by then he should leave before he actually killed him.

But Wayne never quit; on and on his mouth went. He was so upset his brother ignored him he took a knife out of the drawer and threw it at the door. The damn thing went right through the hollow wooden door. Good thing Mark wasn't flat against it cause the blade was sticking out a good two inches on his side.

My brother and I didn't hear about this event from either one of them or their younger sister Missy. Oh, everyone else in town heard the story for weeks; word for word.

No, we never heard about it because we saw it. We walked in their house about five minutes after Wayne threw the thing. They were still screaming at each other when Missy let us in.

We just looked at each other and had the same thought, "And we thought we fought."

I couldn't help but think one of them or maybe both would now be in deep shit. That's the weird thing about a fight with your sibling. After it's over you kind of know you're both gonna get in trouble for it. But you go ahead and duke it out anyway.

Maybe we're no different than those politicians. We must be a little different; we always do our own fighting. We don't send some kid younger than us, say a six year-old, to fight our battles. I guess now that I think about it we probably could have; does this mean I have a future in politics?

Needless to say the D'Amicos didn't hang around each other. Why would they? They were typical kids just like the rest of us.

The Winters brothers fit the bill as we all did. John was less than two years older than Mike and he could hardly stand to be around him. They didn't seem to have the knock out brawls like the rest of us and I always attributed that to them always working.

They didn't have time to schedule a boxing match or fistfight two to three times a week. They were busy making money and a good future. Though the language they spoke to each other was the most inspiring I had ever heard.

The guys in the neighborhood that didn't have a brother to pick a fight with would fill the void by attacking some other boy not in our circle. Sports at school was often a place for them to let loose and alleviate the built up tension.

I often thought they had it bad if they weren't raised with a sparring partner. Well, I could be wrong if that partner were three years older or a hundred pounds heavier.

I've heard of guys with just sisters getting into some major scuffles. I've also heard that the girls win just as many times as the boys.

It was nice to live in a country where one brother can beat the piss out of another. This was Nature's way of training us youngsters for the times to come. We were all born in the Fifties and we were fighting from the first day. We were still fighting in the Sixties and I was positive at the time we'd be fighting in the Seventies.

You always hear that life in the home can mimic the lives we see on television. Maybe Hollywood was simply showing us a reflection of how we lived.

We watched the set at night and went to the Drive-ins on the weekends, just to see how our team won the war. It was educational getting to view all the new moves and weapons. Only the biggest of the stars were entitled to the weapons of the future.

It was definitely an honor, a privilege; to be the first with a new gadget. Movie stars couldn't get top billing if they didn't have the newest gun in their hand for the promos. I always wanted to be in tune with the latest guns, chokeholds and explosives.

At this particular time in my life, Nineteen Sixty-Eight, I can say I didn't abide by the norm of society and fight as much as I should. My demeanor was always on the mellow side; I didn't need the green tobacco to relax my disposition.

Most people would say I was actually easier going than most. But when I was provoked in an aggressive manner I would usually do what was the easiest acceptable thing to society; throw a punch. It only took one for most offenders to back off.

For some strange reason it seemed that Mark, Al and I had the same actions leading to our household scuffles. The three of us were stronger and bigger than our live-in sparing partners. Yet a law of Nature, that was true back then and still is today, allows the smaller person to somehow have a more annoying, provocative, irrelevant, incompetent, immaterial and just plain asking-for-it mouth.

Al called it "brotherly love" when he tangled with Gary. He told me he loved his brother so much that when he asked for something he gave it to him. I didn't realize at fourteen that Gary was asking to get the crap knocked out of himself so often.

It took me a couple of years to admit I loved my brother just as much. When he asked for it I obliged by giving it to him also. That saying I learned in church is so true. "It is better to give than receive." I never did know my brother's opinion on that quote from The Bible.

I see the younger brothers and sisters of today and wonder if they fight like we did back then. I expect they would, if not do a better job of it. They have been immersed in war just as much as we were those fifty years prior.

Only difference today is that the media makes the wars out to be some kind of honorable profession. Kids today choose not to go to college; whereas my generation was drafted out.

In Nineteen Sixty-Eight, when boys were getting killed and blown all to pieces in a land that didn't want us there, the teens left behind tried to help. We tried to protest, vote, and learn the facts about why we sacrificed our own for total strangers.

We forced the media and the politicians to answer questions. They tried so hard to keep the body counts and the truth about how much we were "needed" and "wanted" by those foreign governments secret. They don't bother doing that today; nobody cares to ask.

Perspective of living and dying seems to be directly proportionate to the status of a draft. If your friends are being commandeered and thrown into a battle it's one thing. The drafted didn't ask for a war, didn't believe in a war, and didn't think they should have to die needlessly for some other country.

Obviously in the past years, the years of my youth so different than today, a war sustained and nourished by a draft would harbor feelings which are totally different than today.

The soldiers of today appreciate and joyfully go to battle and can't wait to get in the thick-of-things. I can't think of one anti-war rally in the last twenty years; maybe they do it on social media.

# Chapter 3: Sunday

Church service was over at eleven-thirty which put us back home a little past noon. My father would have taken us to lunch before heading back home, but my brother and I had made plans with the Rileys to go fishing.

My parents were real sticklers when it came to keeping the spirit of the Church alive in us. Years later I learned from my father that when one of his ships was kamikazed in his War he prayed to God he'd never miss Church again if he lived. Need I explain more?

We were changed and across the street with our gear in record time. Al had already loaded all their stuff in the car, so as soon as he heard the dog barking he was out and putting the key in the ignition.

This was one of the few activities we all four did together. Al would never let the two Garys go to the City or any other sophisticated clubs with him because they usually got too wasted and rowdy.

Al always said. "They're in the larval stage of becoming rednecks."

To keep the fighting to a minimum I would ride in the front with Al; while Gary and Gary fooled around in the back. Law and order were usually the mood of the ride when going hunting or fishing. That was unless something like wrong directions, a missed turn or forgetting the food and bait on the porch interfered with the peace.

Probably the worst fight to ever breakout in that Plymouth was on one occasion going to the Flat Brook.

We had left the house around three-thirty after staying out until one drinking in a few discos. Leaving this early in the morning assured us we'd be able to stop for breakfast and make the stream by daybreak.

Most of the hour and a half drive was behind us when the most stupid, unwise, imprudent, absurd, and dumbest driving maneuver I'd ever seen in my entire life was performed.

First I'll explain that we were no more than maybe fifteen minutes from one of our favorite diners near Sparta.

The day temperature had risen well into the low nineties and back then most cars didn't have air. We could only tool along at forty to fifty on the back country roads, so to keep cool we had the front vents open and all windows cracked.

The ride was a little warm and humid, but tolerable. After all; sausage and eggs were only ten miles away. That was until the proverbial shit hit the fan. Literally.

Within smelling distance of those eggs frying Al slows to a stop, so as not to run over a mother and her litter of three baby skunks. They were doing what most animals do when the air gets cool and the pavement holds the heat from the day before. They were all sprawled out; trying to enjoy a warm early morning nap. Don't forget, they're nocturnal.

With the low beams now bearing down on them, like a roaring freight train, Al inches up to them and lays on the horn.

Oh yeah; he blasts those polecats good. The mother does what a mother skunk always does. Her children may have been small, but not too young to understand and join in. They pissed. I mean they all pissed on that front end of that car. Al and I frantically tried to slam the vents shut; while not puking.

To this day I don't know how he closed the vent, rolled up the window and floored it in reverse; actually leaving rubber. We were gassed like the soldiers in the trenches back in WWI.

Unless you've been through it; you have no idea. Not only are you choking, but your eyes swell shut. So after he drives on the one inch wide shoulder to avoid getting sprayed again we fly at sixty plus to the restaurant. One of the Garys did heave out the window, and no Al didn't slow down.

The moans in the backseat were more of a coughing type and the words were mostly of the typical garden variety after an event like this. Both Garys were saying something to the effect that in less than a year they'd be driving, and this was the last time they'd get in a vehicle with Al.

I couldn't say the same thing; I had longer to go. Al would have stopped sooner, but the restaurant was so close.

We all left our windows open and entering the restaurant took one of the few tables left. We order three coffees and a tea for Al. We gave the waitress our food order at the same time.

Within seconds, I mean I've never in my life had such fast service, she appeared with our drinks. They were all in paper to-go cups.

She informed us, "Here, these are on the house. The management would appreciate it if you boys wouldn't mind waiting outside for your orders. And please stay away from the door. I'll call you when they're ready."

Never did occur to any of us what we looked like; let alone smelled like. When we hit the sidewalk we could smell skunk as if they were right at our feet. The smell seemed to fill the square of the quaint little town.

Al may have parked a good two blocks away; it was still one hundred miles too close. Gary and Gary started walking back toward the car mumbling profanities I never knew existed.

The boys in the backseat were bitching so much that Al diverted our destination to a nearby lake. The water would be warmer, and fishing was to become secondary to swimming.

Gary asked his brother if he'd stop for some kind of soap or shampoo. Al's only response was where did he expect to get soap at six in the morning. He added he thought he had seen some Windex in the trunk.

I guess as far as I can remember that day didn't turn out all that bad. I didn't have a fight with my brother and neither did Al with his. It was common to go a day or two without a confrontation.

It usually wasn't the big stuff that precipitated a brawl; it was more the little shit. You can understand how what seems as minor nagging, pestering and instigating can fester into a major conflict. My parents always told me to ignore him and he'd go away. Trouble was he didn't. Not until I gave him one good punch.

Al called me a couple of weeks after that to come over and we'd go down to the river fishing. My brother decided he wanted to go also which was fine with us. When we arrived at the back porch my brother pointed to the glass door. Well, it was a glass door yesterday.

Al rushed right out and told us to watch where we walked, and he was certain Gary wasn't coming. My brother gave Al a stupid inquisitive look and Al explained that Gary was upset he wouldn't take him down to his cousin's house.

Al pointed to the door as we started walking, "Think he was mad? After he slammed it there wasn't one piece of glass left. It all came flying out."

I kept thinking all the way to the river that the only reason they didn't escalate to all-out war was probably due to all the broken glass on the ground. I know if it was the D'Amico's door that wouldn't have stopped them.

Here we have another example as to the limits a person or country will go to for a war. One person's limit can be miles above or below another's.

In the case of war in the time of chivalry; battles were only fought during the daylight hours. In the times of the Sixties; battles were not fought over pieces of broken glass.

Nice to know we have gained some ground on becoming a civilized people. Maybe someday we won't bomb cultures or nationalities whose broken lives are walking on fields of squalor and irreparable despair.

I tried to read all the small newspapers circulated by the so-called "Hippy" movements that Al would give me. He would collect them from everywhere. His friends in college were his number one source, but they could even be found at the bowling alleys and grocery stores.

The one common theme of every one of those papers that seemed to hit me the hardest; no matter if it was anti-war, anti-establishment or anti-segregation, was how one group always wanted control over another person or persons. This similarity would make me think about other cultures, races, religions and nationalities like nothing I was exposed to before.

They all listed the same manifestations of fear; bigotry, jealousy, superiority, inferiority, and hypocrisy. These words sounded to me to be exactly the same words I used when trying to understand why I myself needed to get into a battle or go to war.

It had never occurred to me before that governments and so-called radical groups have the exact same precipitating thoughts as I did before joining in the game, the action, or the battle.

The way I perceived my brother's actions, the way Gary perceived Al's, the way John perceived Mike's, the way Wayne perceived Mark's and vice-a-versa; was nothing less than how the members of the United Nations perceived each other.

How could this be? The smartest, most elite thinkers of the day thought the same as a fourteen year-old from the suburbs of the City. If what I have just stated is in fact true; God help us all.

I know I was born into a world of war, as a fish is born into a world of water; we know of nothing else. Will someone please tell me that the leaders of the world we live in are smarter, more tolerant, more sharing, more forgiving and certainly more compassionate than a group of fourteen to seventeen year olds who jump down each other's throats at the least bit of provocation? I can only imagine, if I live to be a hundred, that my plea will still be unanswered.

Getting back to those Un-American, irreverent, subversive and revolutionary newspapers of the Sixties. I had to agree mostly with the mainstream, middle class, White Anglo-Saxon Protestant view; didn't I? After all I was a WASP.

How dare these groups, some with longhair, some with Afros, and some with shaved heads; envision an American society without the salvations of war? How am I to keep my brother in check without the overhanging fear of retribution? Am I not my brother's keeper? Even the lion tamer may sometimes have to use his whip.

I now understand why all those newspapers from the Sixties died out and why we haven't changed our view as a country on the ways of war. It's part of us; it's in our blood.

Wouldn't we, as a nation, need a complete transfusion if we were to embark on a path of less fighting and more understanding. Think of the insurance bill that would entail. Trying to covert an old, tired, boxer of a nation into a young, lean, educated, mentor to our own young and the young of the World.

Think how expensive it would be to transform a nation of unemployment, arms and coercion of other governments into a nation of education, work, and respect for other nations.

How could we even ponder the idea that saving money in the bank as a country would be more profitable and secure, than stashing warheads in mountain bunkers and on the high seas?

I can say from experience, that when my brother and I weren't fighting, we could save a lot of money together. Enough to get a Johnson engine or a new boat. Think those Hippies may have been right; it pays not to fight?

# Chapter 4: Monday Morning

I could hear the rain pouring down in buckets, which meant a reprieve from work today. Feels like it's been forever that I had a Monday off. I turned toward the alarm clock thinking if I didn't move an inch it would kick on in about three minutes. I could tell my brother was already watching TV, so I chilled waiting for the familiar click sound, then the music.

"Sunday! Sunday! Sunday!" God how I hated that Monmouth drag race commercial. It had me rolling over and turning the dial like a blind squirrel on acid. I was frantic to turn to another station, helplessly my fingers kept slipping off the knob.

At one point it rested on ABC's Cousin Brucie. Taking a breather I left him on for a while. He was a real OK guy, but the music was more of the Pop kind; not too much Iron Butterfly or Clapton.

After spending more time out of my young life listening to Tim's "Tiptoe Through The Tulips" than I really wanted to, instead of hanging myself with my bed sheets, I continued spinning that ivory knob.

One channel I scanned was talking about the mood of the country. For some unknown reason I held the dial there and after a few seconds let go.

I recognized the voice, though I couldn't connect the face that went with it. This always bugs the shit out of me, so I listen more intensely trying to connect that familiar voice with a face.

The commentator was interviewing what sounded like a young black man and women. Each stated they were from north of the City, yet the young lady sounded more like my Aunt Irene; she lived in Queens.

Anyway, they were discussing one of the most heated topics in our country at the time. Basically the three of them were asking and answering each other's questions and perspectives as to why, we as Americans, can't just get along with each other.

I'll never forget what the lady said when she made her comment after being asked about our blossoming space program. She spoke so intelligently; I think even the Grand Wizard would have listened.

Her answer to the interviewers question went something like, "I'm all for the space program. This new science will lead to breakthroughs in health, chemistry and things mankind has never even dreamt of. The more we learn about who we are and where we've come from; the more we may all learn we're stuck with each other on this hunk of dirt and water called Earth.

I do pray though, if our men going into space ever come across another type of people, they resemble those people. It would be horrible if they didn't. Just think what might happen to them; wearing different clothing, speaking differently and looking differently. Yes; that could pose a very viable risk."

She had my ears and brain cemented to that station. I listened to three various opinions of what our society at the time was thinking.

That commentator had titled his show perfectly. They were discussing a "Mood" that everyone else was trying to either ignore, until it went away, or cover-up.

I was only fourteen at the time and even I was old enough to know that ignorance is not bliss. Ignorance is being stupid, uninformed and most of the time dangerous.

The young man spoke of the Revolutionary War, the Civil War, the Spanish-American War, the First World War, the Second World War, the Korean War, the Vietnam War and a War not yet named. This unnamed War, he most sorrowfully thought and explained, was by far the most destructive to our nation and its people.

When he gave his examples it had me frozen in a place where I didn't want to be. I tried as hard as I could, lying in that bed, to project my body and soul to another time; another place. If I could have only jumped twenty or so years into the future; all this war and its misery would certainly be extinct by then.

I was aware of some of the events and names he spoke of. I would read the magazines and newspapers left by the customers at the Sub Base. Some days I was privileged and would get the Wall Street Journal and Times; both with that day's date.

The Journal had a lot more U. S. and world news than most people realized. I guess the price kept them from finding out what a fine, reliable publication it was.

Listening to the words flow out of his mouth about the early Sixties was as mesmerizing as listening to my Grand-Pap's stories of the Great War and the following Great Depression.

His deliberate hesitation in the way he answered the questions was intense. I could visualize his face contemplating his thoughts before he spoke. Oh, how I wish my brother had his talents.

When the man doing the interview made the comment about how young he and the lady were, this man with the voice of an educated, well-mannered spokesman simply replied, "Age in this respect may be a hindrance. Sometimes as we get older we get accustomed to our surroundings. Even if these surroundings may be a prison or a lonely senior-citizen apartment. With age we no longer strive for change as much as we accept our reality; the here and now.

Time. And I believe you would agree we me on this; does have a way of cooling down the fire. It slowly changes our Mood. Yes. Our Mood of a hope of a better tomorrow is exchanged for a more realistic Mood. A Mood of complacency and despair".

He expounded on his explanation of age by listing names of other young men who have tried to elevate the "Mood" of the country. After hearing the first three names I could tell where he was going. And it wasn't a very pleasant place.

For his complete list of young men was quite a somber list. The interviewer never even made a breathing sound. I could only assume that everyone working in their radio studio was listening to what everyone tuned in on the radio was listening to. I may have been off from school that Monday in July, but I was going to get one hell of an education.

His list started with a man who had died at the age of forty-six. A president who acted on what he believed; all men should be treated with the same respect and dignity. This man was steadfast in his view that all Americans were entitled to the same opportunities. He used all the resources available to him at the time. Time just wasn't on his side. Actually; I think we've all suffered when his sands ran out.

Next was another man, a Mr. Little, who died at the age of thirty-nine. He was tired and fed-up of waiting for Hope and Respect to arrive out of nowhere. He had waited thirty-nine years; should he have waited another thirty-nine?

There was a saying the older folks would tell us back in the Sixties, "Someday your ship will come in".

I bet the oceans of the world would have run dry as the Sahara before his ship ever hit the docks. Sometimes when you're not as complaisant as others think you should be; you suffer for it. And he certainly did.

When he spoke of Ben Brown, a twenty-two year-old truck driver, it brought back memories. I had read about him in the papers last year.

He was born on May 12th and died on May 12th. An innocent bystander shot in the back after picking up a sandwich on a cool May evening.

I told myself upon hearing this that the man on the radio was absolutely right about our country's "Mood". I never told anyone that listening to that show really changed my "Mood", and forever.

I never felt comfortable at another anti-war rally after that. I always had that slight fear of being shot. It may have been a longshot, but a shot no less.

Then there was this preacher, who died at the age of thirty-nine. He too died because he wanted people to get along with each other. All this man ever wanted was peace to shine down on our America.

Funny thing about this man was when I'd hear him speaking on the television or radio; he always used the term "Our". He spoke only of the things that were so overly abundant to me, a fourteen year-old in New Jersey, yet were obscenely scarce to an eighty year-old somewhere else. Was he so off base?

The youngest man, really still a child, he spoke of was dead two weeks shy of his eighteenth birthday. This was probably the strangest and hardest of all of these to comprehend.

I couldn't understand how he got shot; if he weren't over in Nam. We weren't at war with California; were we? This happened the first week of April and I don't remember seeing the name Robert Hutton in the news. Then again; government censoring was at its peak in the Sixties.

He capped off his list with the one I now suspected would be last and was right. The forty-two year-old brother of the President. It had been two months and yet I couldn't see anything good coming from that horrific event. Was I missing something? If whoever did this act thought it would improve the "Mood" of our country or that of the world's; I wish they'd explain it to me.

When the interviewer's voice returned I, and everyone else listening, could hear the slight tremble. When we listened to radio back then we really listened. Plus; where I lived we could see the City skyline at night. That meant the radio waves were always loud and clear. I could tell I wasn't the only one educated on the subject of the "Mood" of our country and how young men are in the forefront.

I couldn't help but believe after that radio show that the men, over the age of fifty who controlled our country, were somehow against our own citizens.

Can two separate groups in our great society be that unhappy, unsure and distrusting; as to absolutely love our homeland and yet despise our leaders? Was America ready for another revolution where all people are equal, and war is not the answer to every problem?

The Sixties was the time to live if you really liked war. It was around one hundred-ninety-two years and eleven days ago that our country started its first war and it wasn't to be its last. Now it was apparent, after all the time that has passed, we are no longer satisfied with declaring war on other nationalities.

We're declaring war on whatever faction of American society meets the general description of an internal enemy. Those traitors to our way of life that believed in rights for all American citizens or had such unholy views as to believe "War Is Not The Answer" will be tolerated no more.

I was only fourteen at the time, though I was more than half-sure the politicians were thinking they had such a good handle on Korea and Vietnam. Why not try the same brilliant tactics in Newark, Chicago and L. A.?

These guys down in D. C. had the blessing of the American public when it came to these wars. They were almost giddy with the anticipation of starting another war right at home.

I bet those sacred Halls of Congress must have smelled like a government nursing home; those distinguished men wetting themselves in all their excitement.

We were gonna have another war; Hallelujah! Here in the States where all Americans could even be part of it. No more watching from the sidelines.

I was taught in history class that the senate in the time of Rome was composed of thinkers and dreamers. Our senate, at this time, was filled with bullies and hawks who liked to fight. Let me explain that better.

Sure "They" liked to create a battle, but always had someone else doing the actual fighting. Their primary patriotic action in the fighting was to stay in Washington and buy stock in the munitions and war-machine companies. This was the American way to support the war effort.

They couldn't send their own children to Nam to fight. How could they? They were needed here at home to coordinate the investing into these various growing profitable companies.

I know for a fact they were greatly patriotic because they were greatly rewarded. Of course, with this most recent development on June sixth, maybe a few of them may want to rethink their stance on some of these highly patriotic issues.

# Chapter 5: Monday Day

Rain days were sort of "what" days when I was a kid. What the hell am I going to do all day? Farm work was cancelled and all my friends would be working. My brother and Gary Riley would be lying around all day, but they didn't want me around. So much for them; their loss. I was feeding my fish, frogs and turtles and it hit me; Schultz is home.

His parents and grandparents kept him full of chores and he earned money doing them. I was certain today was his day to work on the garage, which due to the climate was sure to be postponed.

I called down to his house and was quite shocked to hear his grandmother tell me he was out in the garage working. Maybe he'd get soaked or maybe he'd get electrocuted. With his track record it was more likely he'd get both.

I did everything I possibly could around the house to keep from exposing myself to the elements. And yes, boredom finally took over. It may have been like a hurricane outside, but it was still July.

I had on shorts and a T-shirt and I ran like hell down the hill. He heard my sneakers stomping in the water puddled on the driveway and opened the garage as I approached. In the seconds it took me to get the ten or so feet he looked as wet as I was.

His father had asked him to clean and paint some shelves along the back wall. The cleaning part was finished, and he was about to open the can of paint when he asked me if it was a good idea. I told him I thought it was too humid and maybe he'd be better off waiting at least until the deluge subsided. He slapped that can down on the floor and yelled "Come on". He opened the door and calmly strolled to the house.

He might have been a year older than me, almost an adult at fifteen, but he was still a kid when it came to work. He ran to his room to change and told his grandmother he couldn't work in the rain. She didn't argue one bit. He asked her for a quarter and of course she gave him a few dollars. We were off; to where I had no clue.

Where do kids go when it's raining cats and dogs? Schultzie's plan was the bowling alley. Yeah, he knew we'd look like shit by the time we got there, but why not?

What else was there to do? Besides with his money, my money and the five bucks from Babci; we were in great shape.

Yards before the Lanes was a small pizza place; LaBella's. He grabbed my arm as we walked by and said something to the affect that we could get warm. I didn't debate; I ran for the door.

The food was great, and the dry heat was even greater. We sat there long enough for a couple of slices apiece and a dry ass. He was telling me with his mouth full that the rat-screwing prick at the bowling alley wouldn't rent us shoes if are feet were wet. Mrs. La Bella heard him and threw down another slice in front of each of us; on her.

His descriptive usage of the English language had no bounds. I've heard him call many grownups words I wouldn't even attempt to spell. Maybe she wanted to keep him eating and unable to speak; it didn't work. He could cuss like a sailor; even if his mouth were glued shut.

Of all the guys I grew up with he would have, what many people called, the most colorful language for a teenager. Oh, it was colorful alright.

One time when his brother was home from college the two were going at it pretty good. I tried and tried to remember some of his adverbs and adjectives. Finally, when I couldn't remember them that night before bed, I went downstairs and called his house. He told me he'd have to tell me the next morning; his mother and father were right in the room watching TV.

As in my case, similar to most kids younger than the rest of the crowd, when the older guys would call me something derogatory; I'd just walk off.

Not Schultz; hell no. He would let fly a barrage of words that were foreign to most of the guys sixteen to sixty. They would get so mad because they didn't know what he called them that they'd chase him for blocks. Most often he'd get away, but not always.

You'd think even with those one out of fifty times of getting treated to a can of Whoop-ass he'd hold back just a smidge. No way with Frank. Ain't gonna happen.

No-one likes to see a friend get harassed or threatened by a much bigger kid. Yet, it always turned out to be something of an education for me. I couldn't figure out if it were because he had always stood up to his older brother. He must have been tired of somebody four years older and much stronger always forcing their way.

As he was getting older, he was getting stronger. We all could see he was going to be a force to reckon with in the years to come. If he wouldn't take shit from people at fifteen; I could guarantee he wouldn't be taking it at eighteen.

He beat me at all five games, and I could tell he was even trying to let me win at least two at the end. He was always good to have around cause he always shared what he had like the rest of us. He never hesitated to assist in a verbal or physical way.

I bet if Uncle Sam would have seen him playing war at the age of ten they would have tried to enlist him then. Oh, did I use the wrong term? I meant draft. No chance in hell he'd enlist.

He'd fight if he had too, but wars of his own making. I guess he always did fight for his friends too. Back then, I don't remember him or any other kid on our street, calling Uncle Sam one of his friends.

The monsoon had all but stopped when we left the Lanes to start the walk home. Moving along at a relaxed pace we were sure we'd be home by five. Bowling does a job on one's appetite; even after three slices of pizza, one cheeseburger, fries and who knows how many drinks. I was about to leave him in front of his house when John pulled over to our side of the curb.

He lowered the music and asked if we were going to be at the ball field tonight. I couldn't help looking all around at the puddles everywhere and the stream of water still rolling down the street as if it were a natural mountain spring.

Schultz shrugged his shoulders as if asking "why" and I held back waiting for his response. There was no way we'd be able to take the field even if the sun came out for an hour or two. It was just too wet.

Schultz pointed to a little lake that had formed one house down on the corner. That storm drain was basically useless. Four more houses down was the brook, which always flooded. Needless to say the pond, of at least twenty by twenty size, wasn't going anywhere for at least another twelve hours.

John shook his head explaining he didn't want to play baseball; he needed us for a kind of meeting. He told us who else would be there, which only assured our positive replies.

He pulled off leaving Schultz and I standing in his driveway wondering why the older kids wanted us to join them. Schultzie was ecstatic. I couldn't help hoping his family had already eaten.

When he got this way he'd eat more than three times his usual amount. I could see the look in his eyes getting hungrier and hungrier.

I started to move, and he laughed, "I guess we'll meet Meat there. I'm sure it's gonna be another one of the secret operations like the bottle run. Later."

I hadn't thought about the bottle run in years. I wasn't more than eleven when that golden opportunity arrived at my doorstep. It was the brainchild of Mike Winters.

Mike had the most brilliant economic smarts of any one I knew. He was into every conceivable mode of making money a sixteen year-old could be in. And even some a thirty year-old wouldn't even venture to try.

He persuaded Al to join in his amphibious night operation mostly because he too had a row boat. The teams involved at the time were Al and Schultz in Al's boat and Mike and I in my boat.

We waited until after nine, in the cover of dark, and rowed across the river to a soda bottling plant. They stacked all the empty cases of bottles along the river. We would take ten cases per boat and head back home. Only one trip at a time; we weren't greedy.

The twenty cases gave us a total of two hundred and forty bottles. At the going value of five cents apiece for the large bottles that gave us a whopping reclaimable cash amount of twelve bucks. When divided by four each rower or as Mike liked to call ourselves, entrepreneurs, received three dollars. Not bad, not bad at all.

The thriving business only lasted three crossings I'm sad to report. They put a rather high chain-link fence around the entire complex. It was so shiny and tall we could see it from our bank of the river.

Walking up the hill it gave me time to think about another money-making scheme the older kids got me and Schultz into.

Mike, Al and John had found some places where we could mine for copper. Yes, real copper. The stuff that was going up in price more and more every day. There was such a demand for the material that was as necessary to war; as oxygen was to life on earth.

We didn't even have to go underground for it. We could mine it in the afternoon sun or wait until early morning when the air was calm and cool.

This soft pliable brown metal, that would turn green if left to the elements, was used in everything from bullets to tanks. Every civilized country on the planet needed it for their very survival.

It was more sacred than gold. Nobody shoots you with a gold bullet; except maybe that Ian Fleming character. With high demand came high dollars. For us kids it was just another opportunity for cash.

On certain mornings, the different municipalities around our area would have a day when people could throw away large items. Such as sofas, shelving, refrigerators, and stoves. The towns would send their men out with large flatbed trucks to haul these big items away to the dump.

Al would drive us to the particular town that had their day and we'd walk the streets early in the morning searching for anything with a motor. A motor meant copper wiring. That was all we wanted; the coil.

While one kept lookout the other would unscrew the panel and remove the coil. Speed was of the utmost importance. It seemed a patrol of other men traveled these same streets in search of used household goods that could either be resold the way they were or refurbished.

They did have a point when they would chase us street urchins for blocks screaming, "Drop that freakin coil you bastards."

I was too young at the time, maybe eleven; I didn't comprehend the value of the intact washing machine or refrigerator. Trouble was we didn't always think that much into things. A good example of that would be the daytime mining at the mountain.

The mountain produced as much, if not more copper, than the coils. It was a dump located on one side of the highway in a remote industrial park.

We'd crawl through the various materials in search of the precious metal in any form. Mostly we'd get bare copper wire; occasionally we'd hit the Mother-load. When one of us struck copper pipe it meant a consolidated group effort to mine the neighboring area.

We'd pool all our finds together and take them over to the weigh-station on the other side of the highway. Everything was shared equally; that's just the way things were back then.

The man who weighted and paid was always friendly and cheerful. After mining for nearly a year it never crossed my mind once that he actually owned the mountain across the way that we were mining. He must not have minded too much. We kept getting paid and he kept getting the cleaned copper.

Mike was definitely the one in charge of our corporate ladder; if we had one. He chose who would be included and to what extent. He was keenly aware, like his brother, of which of us was trustworthy and willing to work.

He wanted a good worker; although he did value brains and ingenuity above all. He was smart like his older brother John. His ability to grow an income was only stymied by his one major flaw; he couldn't be in two places at once. There were times he would try. I know, I was with him.

I know a lot of his ideas may have come from his brother who was slowly drifting away from our small tight circle of friends. John was getting to be more like Bingo and Al. They were all nearing that grand vacation lottery, which put their names in the pot of catastrophe to be drawn for the lucky voyage.

I was fourteen and I often thought about what would happen to my brother and myself. I can't even fathom how these guys must have felt. At least when you're on death row you know your future. In the Sixties a boy lost his future around the age of twelve.

By the age of thirteen most kids, who had half a brain, summed up their next few years as "Who Cares". Would anyone in their right mind stay in at night and study to get an A on a test or get an after-school job to save money for college; or maybe a car? Why would you even think of wasting what time you had left on such trivial things as making plans for any kind of future?

Your chances of a future were slim to none if you came from a middle-class family and didn't have any political connections. There were the few that did what was thought of as crazy back then; study. I know this for a fact; I was one of them.

My brother, like many his age, put their time in at school during the day and their time in at getting wasted during the night. It wasn't like you couldn't get alcohol, drugs or weed anywhere; at any time.

The college kids could see the writing on the wall more clearing than us kids and they reread the message over and over to us younger guys. "Just like in the movie with Rhett Butler, after all...tomorrow is another day. If Uncle Sam doesn't get you today; he'll get you tomorrow!"

My brother would tell me the simple facts when I asked him about how easy it was for all of us to get served in all the bars. He was right about one thing when it came to most of the bar owners and managers; they had all served in either World War II or Korea.

Some were even proud to say they had a son, grandson or nephew serving in the rice fields. This pride was so strong they couldn't wait to let us all huddle back in the corner by the pool tables while they served us Buds in a cold long-neck bottle.

You could read the faces of some of the older bartenders and men at the bar as if they were your parents. Their broad smiles and hilarious jokes only covered the sadness in their eyes momentarily. They knew some of us were doomed.

They had ridden that ride themselves some twenty-seven years before.

I could tell, maybe more than the others cause I didn't drink as much, that when we entered all these different bars the temperament always changed. I had noticed the same reaction when at a funeral. Everyone seems to get quiet when the spouse or parents of the deceased enters the room.

These heroic brave men who had served their country, my country, our country, so valiantly on the battlefield; now couldn't look a sixteen year-old boy in the eyes.

Their stories of the Battle of the Bulge and Wake Island would be put on hold until we again departed the premises. The conversations they would never talk about at home with their families had to wait and be shared only with another who had been in the same situation.

Their bolstering war stories gave them an avenue to drive the haunting realities far, far away. The lost friends, the lost years, the lost pieces of bodies and the ever present nightmares sat in the trunk of their verbal vehicles as they relayed the same story each night to their same buddy.

Exchanges of events that family members would think of as redundant and boring; served as the antidepressant and spiritual elevator of the Sixties.

Every one of these men had our respect and some our sympathy.

Most of the guys that were near graduation were drinking and partying rather heavily I remember. I often thought I hoped they didn't turnout like some of the heroes that we saw holding up the bars; seven days a week.

When I made a smart remark one day to my brother about some of the local drunks and how I prayed we and our friends never became like them he gave me this scary look.

His only words at the time, as far as I can remember, went something like, "God, I hope we all end up like them. You have no clue where we'll be if not. Ass-wipe!"

# Chapter 6: Monday Night

There was no need for me to down my dinner like a starving dog because the rest of the guys wouldn't be over at the field for at least another hour or two.

Bingo and Al didn't get home from work until five, so no way they'd be out before six. I'm sure they could have been out in ten, but it wasn't like we were going after girls or anything as important. I finished my meal and sat on the couch watching the set waiting for Al to call.

My brother came home to change his sneakers and asked if I was ready. He had eaten over at the Riley's and told me they were about ready to go. His joyful news that the rain had finally stopped seemed to get everyone of us wanting to get outdoors as fast as possible.

This would seem strange today I can imagine. Kids around the age of fourteen have their asses glued to a chair while they text like there's no tomorrow. Now that I think about texting. Do you think if we had that back in the Sixties we would have been preoccupied with that and not really cared if we were going to pay a visit to our friends on the east coast of Asia?

My brother and I entered the kitchen and got greeted by Al saying they were ready to move. He had this sort of nervous twitch, as if he couldn't wait to get out of earshot of his parents.

I was getting the feeling that he, my brother and Gary were already apprised of the meaning of tonight's meeting. He was so anxious to fill me in it was killing him. I swear he ran the twenty feet to the bridge; looking back twice to make sure I was keeping up.

We walked a good thirty feet in front of our brothers, and he began to explain why John had tracked Schultz and me down. His description of the summoning could only be taken with a grain of salt at that moment in time.

I could tell he wanted to give me some information, but not the whole ball of wax. Hell, I was thinking I'm not even getting a drip or two. When I stopped before the basketball court he smiled, "Ok, you want it all; don't you?"

"No. Not all. You can leave out the bullshit and narrow it down to the facts. That's not all, is it?"

I think Al was a little surprised when Gary and Gary stopped right next to us. Usually they acted more like we're lepers and walk right on by. My brother only stood there because he heard the word "bullshit".

Al turned around to see who was over by the bench. There they were; those girls that always seem to come around when we played ball. Al wasn't about to say anything in front of them, so standing his ground he started explaining.

"We're going to have a little competition with some guys from over there," he pointed toward our houses which meant he was talking about the town two streets past.

"You guys know Sal Manis; he works with Bingo. He's getting some of his friends and they're going to challenge us to a type of duel. It'll be fun. Meat was telling me about it last night and he said Bingo would get all the details straight with Sal."

My brother and Gary kept staring at the bench, which was normal for them. Gary couldn't care less about what his brother or John wanted to do; he wanted to check out the girls.

Al was getting that disgusted look on his face that he always seemed to wear when his brother and my brother were around. He was slightly more serious than the pair of Garys.

I didn't understand at that instant how serious this small competition was to him. As the evening progressed and the facts came to light even the Garys got with the program and gave their full attention.

Al went over to the window of the school and peering in yelled back that it was already after seven-thirty. He was as confused as the rest of us as to why John hadn't showed up yet. After all, he was the one who got hold of Al, Schultz and I.

My brother spoke up making a suggestion that maybe it had something to do with the fire alarm we heard about twenty minutes earlier. The station was only five blocks from the school.

John's father was a fireman and there had been times in the past when he'd have to take over a business obligation while his father went off to risk his life saving someone else's property.

Thinking, if he hadn't made it to "his" meeting by now, we might as well go; we did. Turned out Gooch was right about the fire. John got stuck doing one of his favorite evening activities, only because his mother and Mike weren't home; babysitting.

The Garys went toward the overpass crossing the highway, while Al and I headed toward the swing. I always thought I was too old and too cool to sit on the swings when I was fourteen; though there were exceptions.

Al really had the hots for one of the three girls hanging around over there and I knew he wasn't about to give up the perfect opportunity. He was like a dog after a bitch; that one blonde neither of us liked fit that description to a T.

I wasn't impressed with the covey he had chosen to stakeout and he was well aware of it.

He'd tell me over and over, "So they're not that great looking. You can fool around anyway; think of it as practice."

Practice? He said the same thing when we went shooting ground hogs.

He referred to them as Viet Cong, "Just look at them as practice."

To this day I thank God and Al himself for getting through those years. Those Sixties and the ensuing Seventies tried their best to beat him down, as they had so many other young men.

Al was nobody's fool and he knew the odds were stacked against kids like us when it came to winning the grand prize. Of course our Government made sure every young man eligible for the jackpot had an equal chance at winning. The small fact that your name had to be amongst the lucky contestants was often overlooked.

Yes, Al had as good a chance in the coming years as Bingo, Mike, John, Gary, Schultz, Wayne, Mark, Gary and myself of winning the all-expense paid trip. This highly sought after misprize was so enviable that most sons of the highly connected by way of money, politics, corporate or religious avenues didn't have to worry about the odds of winning. Their chances of triumph were as secure as the money underneath their daddy's mattress.

Some didn't handle it as well as most of the guys I grew up with in Nineteen Sixty-Eight. The endless and rather inexpensive array of drugs, along with alcohol, left plenty of ways to forget about your chances in the then famous National Lottery.

Most kids today, between the age of twelve and eighteen, haven't a clue as to what I'm talking about; I'm sure. I would even wager a good bottle of Scotch, single malt only, that it would take me years of asking to find one father that has explained in real terms to his son what it was like to live back then.

Why would a father want to admit to his child that there was a time in his life when he didn't have a mortgage or a car payment; yet was so insecure it would make your skin crawl?

Why would a grown man tell a story of sometimes getting up in the middle of the night in cold sweats puking from the stress of what the next national televised event may mean?

Men don't share their feelings of hopelessness and panic with their children.

They probably wouldn't understand anyway. Not unless there was an App for that.

Parents of the Sixties tried to keep a watchful eye, but the world around them was speeding faster than it ever had in the history of Mankind. Their War-Baby children were more educated by the school systems and more savvy with the help of television, radio and countless news sources. While many of the parents of young boys were hiding their fears and resentments of the draft; their sons were doing something about it.

If one couldn't afford a one-way trip to Canada; there was always another trip he could take, and you didn't have to leave home. Cheap and seductive was all the advertising this new product needed.

Just like that commercial on television which beckoned "Fly away with me" it was easier, and you didn't have to get a passport or even pack a bag. One, two, three and you were off.

Off to a place that didn't focus on the stink of blood, gunpowder, shit and Napalm. An escape to a place uninhabited by fear and indecision. If it was only that simple. Some of these so-called journeymen went to places they never really returned from.

Dismal voids resulted in their minds that lingered there the rest of their lives. They loafed about in their almost zombie-like existence from that day on. Making homelessness our newest and fastest growing American residential status.

It could have been worse, I guess. They could have started drinking at the age of twelve. Ending up with a disillusioned future; riddled with rejection and failure precipitated by years and years of drinking.

They were going to die anyway; what did it matter how much they drank? They were kids; not doctors or pharmacist. The drugs, the alcohol and the way they made the future bright, tolerable and achievable; made it all worth it.

Now when I think back at the ones that weren't drafted into the game and the ones that were; I have a hard time differentiating. The scars on the outside all look the same to me. I'm sure if I were to dig deeper, look more closely, I'd see the root cause is widely varied.

The anguish of war can never be appreciated by an onlooker like myself. I sometimes wish I had the ability to see inside, to see the cause of the pain and mental suffering.

But as they say, "You may be sorry if you get what you wish for."

It's written in the history books and I've heard it said in the movies, "War is Hell!"

Sure it's Hell; but why then do so many enlist today. In my youthful days they were eating and drinking every kind of poison to escape it?

The boys and girls today that enlist voluntarily don't serve because of the money; do they? I guess some probably do, but certainly not all.

I'm more of the impression they're lured into the Armed Forces with the rewards of college and an opportunity to fulfill their professional ambitions.

The commercial show the smiles, the poise and the self-assurance that goes with a teenager metamorphosing into a fine young adult.

Please don't hate me for what I'm about to write. Please!

Wouldn't it be better? Couldn't it be better? If these young men and women were granted another way to spin the wheel of the so-called non-Lottery Lottery.

Am I that far from the truth when I ask the question, "Is this your only way out? Is this the only road that will lead you to a promise of a future?

Can't the wisest people from government, corporate and the Hollywood establishments put their heads together and find a more civilized way?"

We do still have the Nineteen Sixty-Eight draft in a way; if only a small remnant at best. Our government no longer has to employ both the carrot and the stick. The stick, the draft, is no longer necessary. The carrot alone will suffice when it's the only thing someone will have to eat in weeks.

The dreams and the hopes of a life different than what we were born into have grown exponentially over the past years. Children no longer view the world as what's within a block or two of their house.

The media has shown them the world; a beautiful world where hard work transforms those dreams into a reality. Why shouldn't every child in school have the right to catapult themselves off their dream into a productive, happy life?

Is the price of an education for every child in school, who has earned it, that much more than the cost of war? Does the math show how spending money in other countries, on their residents medical costs and educations, always out-way what The Bible has always stated; "Charity begins at home."

Why is it the ones, whose soil our government wants so hard to protect, never have a draft or pay the "Carrot" price for our American provided entitlements? I guess it's too much to ask someone to fight for their own homeland; as our Forefathers had done.

I can only write what I am familiar with. The situation of children in the late Sixties was a complete opposite of what I see and hear today.

I can't say I knew of anyone my age or near my age that was "Comfortable" with The War. We were all Americans. Our fathers had fought wars just years before we were born, and our Grandfathers fought wars at the turn of the century. They all though on the lines of us kids; war is certainly Hell.

I guess I'll always thank God that so many of my friends went to the Land of Nam and returned home without any visible scars; outward scars that is.

I'll thank the spirits also for the one's that didn't have to go. Yet some of those show the signs as if they had. And lastly I thank whatever Supreme Source controls our souls, our planet and our forever expanding universe for keeping my ass out of the fray.

Though I was expose to various amounts of shrapnel in the form of drugs and alcohol; Al assured me it could have been a whole lot worse.

He, like I, did listen to the old men talk about the wars. I listened without asking questions. Al, on the other hand, wanted the facts from the horses' mouth. He wanted to know the meaning of war and the truth of war; and as far as he was concerned we were drinking in a stable at Aqueduct Park.

These men, these heroes around us, were as proud as could be that he asked. They told us that no-one else in all their lives had the guts, or nerve to ask.

One man at Januk's told us, "It's like asking a mother how her baby drowned. You really want to know, but you just don't ask."

Another man sitting next to me drank down four shots one night and told us, "If you knew what was waiting at the end of the ride; you'd have jumped off the ship in the middle of the Pacific."

Al was floored when one man answered his question as to how many men did he think he had killed over in France.

The man spoke so calmly, "I don't really know the exact amount. I do know the first one. He was my sergeant. He got his arm blown off and I put him out of his misery."

When the man started to tremble a bit Al stared at me as if asking, "What the?"

I'll never forget what the man then said, "I see that Sergeant every night before I fall asleep."

We kids grew up with war all around us. It was in our homes, on our media and even under our desks at school; when we practiced taking shelter from the bomb.

Some of us tried to understand it and maybe even learn to live with it. It was kind of like living with the Meadow Land's mosquitoes; you don't like them, but you get used to having them around.

So the news of a duel was just that; a duel. Nothing major. After all, Al never said anything about a "War".

# Chapter 7: Tuesday Night

Within sight of the skyline of the greatest city in the world; the masterminds of Gantner downed Pepsi after Pepsi planning their defense of the homeland. The cool and astute John Winters listened cautiously as his brother Mike and Al Riley vocalized their views and concerns of the forthcoming battle.

John had the keen ability to sense the direction of another person's thoughts. He never had to wait for a repeat of the proposal; he absorbed it always on the first time around.

The light from a pole lamp, not far from the bench, gave the surroundings a spooky overcast. It was like an old English flick where the fog was starting to swallow an unsuspecting London.

Gooch, my brother, lifted a hand toward the lamp and drew our attention to the fog now thickening. He reminded us how the soupy air would give the same effect as being on water.

On the river or the lake, even a whisper would cross the distance to the opposite shore; landing on the ear of anyone not legally deaf. The band of strategist heeded his warning and the topic of conversation changed to the Mets, space and of course; the girls.

I don't recollect at all if at that time I stayed awake that night thinking about the impending contention. Maybe at fourteen I was under the misguided impression that we were about to engage in a mere uncomplicated scrimmage.

I don't even think my brother, who was seventeen months older than I, fully comprehended the magnitude of the grievances. I'm sure most of the men at Valley Forge hadn't a clue as to what was on Washington's mind; should they? They had other things to worry about; like trying not to freeze to death or getting back into the house an hour after curfew.

Thinking back of all the players who attended the first round of the conference I can honestly say everyone was accounted for. The roster was shorter than it could have been, but it was the most reliant and capable of the lot. I was only added to the list because for my age I was six foot two and one-hundred and sixty-five pounds.

The band of merrymakers included four pairs of brothers; John(Meat) and Mike Winters, Alan and Gary Riley, Gary(Gooch) and Paul(myself) Gilbert and Mark and Wayne D'Amico. The other members were Frank(Schultz) Nolan and Thomas(Bingo) Boniface.

I don't remember the exact time my brother attained the name "Gooch". It did come in handy though; telling him apart from Gary Riley. They were the same age and went everywhere together.

John Winters somehow was pinned with the name "Meat". I never called him that because I knew he didn't like it. Shit, I didn't like it. He was the oldest at seventeen and yet managed to take my sorry ass all over and treated me decent; despite my age or lack of.

From here on out I will refer to John as "Meat"; only for the purpose of not confusing the reader. I never called him that but being the youngest at the time I was overruled in that department.

If I remember right Schultz called him John also; except when he needed to get his attention right now. For some reason, all the others seemed to like calling him "Meat"; not so much Mike though. I guess he might have tried it once.

Tommy Boniface was in the same grade as "Meat". His name, "Bingo", was always a mystery; not only to me, but it seemed everyone else too.

Bingo's mom was at one time a Radio City Rockette. She taught dance in a studio attached to their house a few doors down the street.

Bingo and a few of the older guys were caught one day peeking through the mirrors at the girls in the dance studio. I still regret I had to be in school that day and miss the show.

Frank Nolan was always part of the gang. We were equal when it came to strength, even with him being a year older than me. He was a grade ahead of me and a grade behind Gooch, Gary and Mike. I hung around with Frank probably more than the others due to our closeness in age.

I would have to swear in a court of law that Frank definitely was the one out of all of us that would take a risk. I never figured it out. Was it that he just didn't mind failing; as compared to not taking the chance and never getting the reward.

He'd be the one to jump on thin ice. The others would say he was stupid; I'd always say he had guts.

When I started working and playing music we drifted apart; like most childhood friends do. He had, I guess, what you would call the most misfortunate of all nicknames; "Schultz". You know, the camp guard Sergeant.

Where I grew up, outside the city, everybody had a nickname. I was only called Paul once; that was when they asked my parents what name to put on the birth certificate over at Hackensack.

From that day on it was Paulie, or Little Paul. How could anyone even think of confusing me with Big Paulie from Lodi; he was an easy three-hundred and seven years older.

I hated it when Al and I went to the Railroad Club in Paterson and the old guys at the bar called me Sottile Paulie. It always sounded like "Saltlick"; the blocks we'd put out in the fields for the cows.

I managed to get back in the house undetected that night about an hour after the lights had come on over by the school. With no school the next day and for most of us some kind of summer work, I can only guess the others were home by midnight.

The older guys, the sixteen to seventeen year olds, would always manage to pull-off their own version of the Sermon on the Mount. By ten o'clock the area would be abandoned, except for the small remaining band. Usually one or two would produce a half pint of something high octane. Within an hour it seemed the booze was coming from every direction.

The bottles that were passed to the left and then to the right always seemed to have a sentence or two attached to them.

Handing the bottle for the next friend to have his turn would sometimes be greeted with, "So tell me again. What happened to Wozniak?" or "That guy was stupid; he should have run. If they stuck your ass driving a gasoline truck north of Saigon; wouldn't you run?"

It didn't seem to matter what kind of event or where it took place back in the Sixties. The time could be ten-thirty at night after a school dance or ten-thirty Sunday morning after Church. If you got three boys, and I mean boys aged twelve to eighteen, together the subject of discussion was The War. There was always a small mention of college after graduation; we liked to dream back then too.

I remember walking home that night through the middle of the farm wondering if the local scrimmage would get over to these highly productive fields. They weren't far from where I was assuming the game would be played.

I was kind of hoping we could have fought amongst the scallions, radishes, and beets. Al and I were probably the only two, on either side, that knew the potential of the beet as a projectile weapon.

By the time midnight had come and gone, I was out to the world. It was a good thing my brother and the other guys had remained out to hold further deliberations on the nearing situation. I know I was sound asleep, and they had enough Graves for the lot of them, but surely they wouldn't waste a night like this not doing something constructive.

If I had gone to never-never land thinking about the "Plan", well I'm certain they had to be thinking about the same thing.

The crew remained intact at or near their favorite bench until they were joined by two guys that had graduated at least two or three years earlier. Both of them smoked, which was such a contrast to the rest of us. All ten of us had tried smoking in all its various forms and strangely none of us let the habit stick.

We did use an occasional cigar while fishing or camping to keep the mosquitoes at bay, but we didn't chain smoke like some nineteen year-olds did back then.

Meat and Al were the most annoyed by the smoke and moved away toward the swings. Once he realized they were going to be on their own for a while Al asked Meat if he had thought out any preliminary plans for the attack.

Meat answered, "You mean for the defense don't you? I think they're going to attack us."

Al was feeling good from drinking his allotted one inch of the bottle, "Yeah Meat. Sure. Any plans?"

Meat shrugged, which gave Al his non-answer answer.

Funny thing about Al was no matter how much he drank you never ever saw him wasted. He could still walk a tightrope or fly a plane if he had to.

Now Meat on the other hand had a different way of handling a good buzz. First he'd start smiling; next he'd get real comfortable, as if a nap were in order.

When Al realized he was asking for the impossible at that moment in time, he smiled out, "We'll figure it out tomorrow after work."

In those days, every kid over the age of ten seemed to have a job. If you were old enough to get working papers you'd get a real job somewhere after school and weekends. If you were of illegal age to work nights and such; you'd work for cash.

Some worked like me, on the farm and in family restaurants, places where the government never could catch sight. Yeah, they didn't want you working at fourteen, but dying at eighteen was just fine.

Al sat on the swing staring straight out in front of him; about a hundred yards. It had been a good four years since he was hauling boxes of produce out of those rows and stacking the truck eight feet high. He knew those fields were full of beets that were about ready to be pulled and slammed in a box.

Trouble with what he was thinking was his cohort wasn't really in the mood for a discussion on war tactics. If only he could explain to someone, anyone; the proper use of vegetables in wartime. He couldn't go back to the bench and talk with the rest of the soldiers; not with those two other guys still hanging around.

He'd have to keep this idea on ice until his meeting the next day. He'd have to wait so long for a simple "yes" or "no" verdict.

Al was one of those types that never stopped thinking. His wheels turned twenty-four/seven. If his mind were one of those damn gerbil wheels the rodent would have been dead of exhaustion in less than an hour.

Yes, he'd wait. Not because he wanted to though. He had no choice in the matter. This delay was pissing him off; he wanted to hear from the jury if using beets in the upcoming battle was justifiable or against the Geneva Convention.

With the announcement of the time almost being twelve the party started to make ready for the trek homeward. It was neat in a way how everyone lived on the same street.

If you started at the bottom of the hill, about seven houses down from ours, you'd find the Winters on one side and the Nolans on the other. Four houses up from there was where Bingo lived. Four more houses on the same side, going up the hill, were the Rileys. We were almost across the street from the Rileys. Lastly; the D'Amicos were another twelve house past the Rileys.

We had our own version of "Our Gang". There was always somebody around to play or work with. I was the youngest, so I was usually the one who was given the honors of throwing the first Torpedo of the summer.

First time I guess I was eight or nine. I had no idea the thing would make such a loud noise; or blow a hole in the road. Sure, all the older guys would disappear right after I threw the thing. I'd have to catch up to them over on another street; didn't matter to me. I had a fast Schwinn.

Then there were the times they'd hunt me down to either shovel snow or rake leaves. I never knew exactly how much they had agreed to do the job for, but I always had a good idea. I don't think I ever worked for less than a fiver. That was a shit-load back then.

We didn't screw each other back in those days. How could we? We acted more like family to the ones that we weren't related to, than the ones who were.

Crossing over the parkway bridge Schultz looked down toward the south at the approaching headlights. He was trying to get a look of the field; the small insignificant space of land nestled between the roadway, the backyards of the houses on our street and the road below hugging the river.

The hour of night didn't give him too much opportunity to get a clear picture, but he could suffice with a beacon of light every twenty seconds. Enough to refresh his memory.

He laughed to the D'Amicos, "Maybe we can hide in your backyard and do one of those Roosevelt things. You know; a San Juan Hill."

Wayne was walking closer to the fence trying to get a better view; as now was everyone else. He laughed, "We'd still be too far. Unless Mike can get over to China Town and get us some good stuff."

They all knew what the good stuff was. Mike was the explosives expert amongst us. He didn't really like to blow things up as much as I did, but he had a true affinity for fireworks.

He would take trips to the City with his parents anytime he could. He'd amass sparklers, Romans, copters; anything and everything all of us guys wanted. All he ever brought back for me was something that was also his favorite.

I'd take the trip with him every once in a while and the selection was huge. But nothing else swayed me from my true love at the time; the Black Cats.

They're still my favorite today. How can you even think of spending your hard-earned money on anything but? They had a great fuse, very few duds, and what a bang. I'd spend hours opening them up and taking the powder out to make a much bigger creation. Yeah, for my money; it was always the Black Cats.

I'll admit I did miss some things the older guys did because I was the youngest; the baby of the litter. But at the same time; just being allowed to be with them on the other seventy to seventy-five percent times was an educational experience.

You can bet your life they had no clue they were actually teaching me something all those times out. And if you believe that; I've got a couple of popular bridges I can sell you real cheap.

I could go on for days giving examples of what I've learned back then and still use today from each and every one of them.

Al showed me just as much about hunting and fishing as my grandfather did; not to mention how to drive. Mike taught me how to trap and skin a muskrat, net flounder and how to use a bow. Lest we forget, him driving home my education on fireworks 101 and 102.

Meat was more of the formal educational type. I remember him saying these words to this older man once as if it were just moments ago, "Don't piss on my back and tell me it's raining."

God; how I love that cliché'. I swear; no BS. I've used those endearing words at least once a week my entire life. They are beautiful; don't you think? So short and to the point. Yes; definitely a Jersey term.

Like I stated before; John had no reason to be so accommodating and nice to me, but he always was. If I ever find out who started calling him "Meat" I'm going to hide a dead fish in their wheel-well; another Jersey thing.

Gary Riley and my brother kind of taught me the proper ways of handling alcoholic beverages. These two would take just a little from every bottle in the house. This way they wouldn't get caught. Trouble with mixing all those different liquors together wasn't so much what they tasted like going down. No, that wasn't a problem at all. It was mostly what they tasted like coming back up.

Many a nights my brother was on his knees praying to the Porcelain-God for forgiveness. Well, I can say I only assumed forgiveness. All you could really hear was the sound of a choking walrus coming out of the bathroom.

Schultz, who was strong for his age, had an older brother who helped to toughen him up in more ways than one. Not only were his muscles in good working order, but he did have half a brain when it came to dealing with some on-the-spot issues.

One time I went with him to a dance where I was at least a year younger than all the others there. Somehow, I never figured it out back then and I still don't know today, he pulled off a miracle.

We didn't have any juice or smokes on us, if you know what I mean, when we got there. We had nothing to bargain with if the situation arose. After all, his mother dropped us off and was supposed to come back and pick us up. So basically we were legal and ready for a typical after school dance. Yeah. Right!

I don't think we were inside more than ten minutes and he's talking to these two girls. I was standing back, most likely looking around; scoping the crowd. He comes over to me with them in tow and what a grin.

He kept going right past me when he said, "Let's go. We'll come back later. Nice; Huh?"

All I could think of was, "Nice; Huh?"

He was crazy. Alright; crazy in a good way. We went outside and strolled for a good hour; he was with one girl and me the other. I don't remember their names or even what grade they were in. I do remember they did have an unopened generic blackberry brandy, two joints one got from an older brother and charitable personalities. When I say they had the ability to share; I mean they shared everything they had.

So, here I am again learning from one of the guys older than me. Maybe Schultz was just a year older; that's all it took. He showed me what happens when you just give in and jump. Take the plunge; head first.

In the years since then I've learned that life is much more interesting if you're willing to take that risk. Sitting on the sidelines was never in his game plan. Yes, he'd certainly man a major position in the battle to come.

The D'Amico brothers were not the most qualified to teach me about fishing or launching a projectile out of a pipe hammered into the ground. These two, one a year older and the other two, didn't have time for the outdoor sports.

They were into music; they lived for this one thing. They had to hear it live and they had to hear it often. I have to laugh to myself every time I think of how loud it was on some occasions. We'd all be deaf by now if it weren't for the breaks that Mark would force us to take.

I learned from these two that music will lead you directly into something else; something even more addictive. When a person plays music it seems that Nature doesn't stick to it's cardinal rules; as scientists would think. There is a noticeable complete breakdown in society as we know it. The rules of the past are just that; rules of the past. The D'Amicos, along with Al and Gary Riley, catapulted me into the post-Beatles era.

I was now swallowed whole by Clapton, Hendrix, Mattress, Spooky Tooth, Stills, Led Zep and the Stones. The harder I tried to learn these songs, the more and more distracted I became.

These other four had untapped a well that was worth a million times more than all the oil in Texas. They had a mantra that was more compelling than even breathing to stay alive. They had the girls. The girls that came from everywhere to hear the music.

I practiced and I practiced. I had to play well enough to be needed, more than wanted, by these four musicians on my street.

I worked and it worked. This was my out. I was now allowed to go to the city, to stay out til midnight and even try my new hobby every weekend; as long as I was with these four.

Now I was starting to understand why the older guys, Al, Meat and Bingo, weren't fishing or playing ball much anymore. They had started this other hobby a few years earlier.

My parents would let me troupe along with these trusted friends of the neighborhood. And why not? They all came from good families. None were convicted of murder or espionage. We were having clean fun.

We didn't get so high or so drunk that we ever looked the part. That was the trick. We did imbibe at times, but never going overboard. I never prayed to the Porcelain-God in our house; I waited until college to ask forgiveness of my sins in that manner.

That summer of the battle I do remember seeing some of my favorite pass-times slowly start to disappear; get replaced. This new hobby they introduced me to was just too much fun. I could tell, even at age fourteen, I'd be playing this sport for the rest of my life.

I was assured by these older guys that I would get more apt and skillful as time went on. They even went so far as to arrange for me to practice some nights. Hell, they never gave me a break when playing Monopoly, but this game was different.

I didn't care now if I ever owned a hotel on Boardwalk. Mark, Wayne, Al and Gary were right; who needs Milton Bradley or Parker Brothers when you've got girls, girls, girls and more girls.

# Chapter 8: A New Game

Northern Jersey, on the City side, had run out of places to build shortly after the Pilgrims arrived at Plymouth. This deficiency of "Improvable" space, for lack of a better term, left the developers no other alternative than to put a building in the middle of a Garden State Parkway exit ramp or some other neglected, forsaken place.

A perfect place to build, only because someone else didn't have the nerve to do it before, was a small acreage that was an island off by itself. It was surrounded by River Road, the Parkway and the backs of the existing houses.

This was an ideal spot to drop a cul-de-sac and maybe three or four houses. It was such a serene and peaceful place, "Yeah, right!"

We were all astonished it took over three-hundred years of civilization to put a house there. Why would Lewis and Clark spend all that time and energy when they had places like this so close to home?

Maybe it was like Al said, "Sometimes you have to step in cow shit if you want to get home in the dark."

The dozers and the earth movers swallowed and regurgitated that small plot of land for what seemed months. They stripped that land down to the topsoil, then sent in other machines to collect and pile it out of the way for future use. After the sewer lines, water lines, the houses and the gravel streets were in place; they'd replace that topsoil around the existing houses.

Topsoil went for big money, so what if a few of the locals were always seen late at night wheeling off a load or two for their gardens.

Where this soil was piled the mounds must have been a good thirty feet high. They had made a few crisscrossing lanes, the width of the dozer, all throughout these hills. I bet there were a good twenty-five or more of them; if you counted the ones that had been run over until almost flat.

Between all these hills were the ruts created from the metal tracks of the heavy machinery. These roadways truly resembled the ones in The Philippines that you'd see in the combat movies on WOR's The Million Dollar Movie on channel nine.

With all the rain we had this spring and the beginning of the summer these ruts or trenches had become a scummy green shallow endless pool. At one time they had small toad tadpoles in them, but now it's just mosquito larvae.

Whenever we'd cut through the hills we would walk around the base of the hills and jump over the large stinky puddles. With the topsoil scraped off the ground, the ruts seemed to hold this water on the surface forever.

The hills themselves were made of almost pure, dark topsoil. If it didn't rain for a few days they would become the consistency of flour. You could hardly climb to the top; even Lawrence of Arabia would have a hard time. If it rained or there was a heavy mist the dirt would get compacted and more easily scalable. This loose, enriched, dark soil was so nutritious; the weeds would grow fast and furious.

It was around the time that school was ending that we discovered what a tropical jungle we had in our own backyards. Literally! These hills were just over the fence behind the D'Amicos. It was Mark who discovered them one day while walking the dog.

I remember him telling everyone how he lost his dog in the "Wilderness" for about fifteen minutes. Seems he was on the trail of a rabbit. The closer Mark got, the further away the rabbit ran. He hadn't a clue his dog was tracking a prey; he couldn't see two feet into the thick, lush vegetation.

Mark and Wayne tried to describe it to us over at the ball field one night. No-one called them liars, though after getting enough looks of "Sure"; they demanded we end the game early so we all go over to their house and see for ourselves.

From my point of view, and I found out shortly everyone else's also, it was nothing short of the pictures we were watching every night of The War coverage from Viet Nam.

I couldn't help telling Wayne I was waiting for the Air Cav to come bursting out in front of us at any moment; it couldn't have been more real. Al kept going on and on about the height of the greenery.

It was almost as if we all were going back in time; even if it was just for five or six years. I could remember those years when I was nine or ten and the oldest in our group was thirteen. There were no driver's licenses, day or after-school jobs, and girls hadn't been invented yet.

Everyone had the same hobby and the same amount of free time. We spent all those hours, days and weeks fishing and boating along the brook and the river and doing what boys do best; play war.

We always had the same kids on the same sides. The rules always stayed the same, as the boundaries grew larger and larger with every new summer. Simple plans of ten-minute battles would gradually escalate into elaborate cooperative operations of hours, as nighttime warfare was granted more and more by our parents.

It was the sport of the century, the national pastime of every child in America at the time. We watched the war movies when it rained or snowed, and we acted them out in the sun. I guess we were just doing what all normal kids do; we were mimicking our surroundings.

We used our smarts and our imaginations for the betterment of all Humanity and our own four block neighborhood. We would be the ones the future would call upon to protect the country. We were all united in one vision back then on our street back in the Sixties; we were ready for war.

Standing at the edge of the jungle I could sense I wasn't the only one standing there thinking, "Man, I wish we had this back when. Think anyone would want to play? Better not say anything, they might laugh."

Go Schultz; yes he was always the one who didn't give two shits if we all laughed at him, "Hey, anybody up for war tomorrow?"

He was a serious as cancer. He didn't say another word and after thirty seconds neither had anyone else.

Wayne started laughing, "Count me in."

The "me toos" were now on the loose. It was as if we suddenly shot back in time.

Al and Mark were almost on the other side of the fence when Mark yelled back, "Same sides; we'll use dirt-bombs. Make sure you wear your sunglasses."

Mike grinned to me, "Shit. I'll get my uncles motorcycle helmet."

So here we were, older; but certainly not the wiser. Do boys really ever grow up when it comes to war. Obviously; the older guys knew something about this couldn't be right, because they didn't jump right on it like they do when they're discussing going drinking.

Still the verdict was in and it was unanimous. Why not drag out the tricycle while we're at it? Isn't that basically the same thing as this?

I could hear my answer as plain as day from the silent soldiers around me, "Hell no! This is War! What are you a Commy?"

One weed in particular thrived in these hills and managed to gain a foothold that even Napalm couldn't dislodge. I'm sure everyone is familiar with ragweed. But this was no regular ragweed. This was a gigantic version of the annual nuisance.

These plants were a healthy green with branches stretching ten feet wide. They would have been wider if not

curtailed by the giants surrounding them. Growing in such
close proximity forced them to act more like a forest, than a
haphazard scattering. They grew like the pine trees on the
Georgia-Pacific tree farms. These hills resemble the Pine
Barrens more than the Watchung Mountains. They were tall,
and they were tough.

When we'd pull on one of the big ones to help get us up a
hill or over a puddle sometimes they'd come loose in the
powdery soil. We were shocked to see that carrot-like root
was almost two feet long.

The thing was as straight below the soil as it was above. It
was the perfect spear; once you took the branches off. Better
yet; why not break it off at knee-height and throw it like a
German hand-grenade. The son-of-a-bitch always went
straight; with or without a dirt clump to help it along.

The best I can remember as to when the weapon of choice
changed from the dirt-bomb to the Whomba was the very
first battle. The topsoil was so powdery we were all
scrambling; trying to get decent size hunks.

Meat and Mike Winters will most likely get the
accommodation for the discovery when it becomes public
knowledge. It was one of those serendipitous discoveries at
best.

Mike was on the team I was on and we were really getting
hammered. Meat was just across from us and laughing that
he was running out of ammo. All at once the laughing
stopped and a huge-ass weed comes flying in my direction.

Meat had pulled the whole sucker out of the ground. I
mean he was winging those fifteen-plus foot long cornstalk-

like things at me. Mike saw what he was going and retaliated the same way.

Meat said later he had broken one by mistake and didn't have time to get another, so he heaved the bottom foot of the stalk with the root ball at us. What a freakin weapon. When that root-ball hit me in the head the dirt exploded like that bomb over Nagasaki.

The dirt below the surface was so dry it exploded into a million fine particles. When that mushroom cloud appeared over my location the whole war came to a stop. Nobody was in the fighting mood any longer; they were collectively laughing their asses off. Oh, I would have been too; if I didn't just get nuked.

So there was the birth of a new weapon and a grand escalation in neighborhood, if not, global arms. War was no longer a game for the eight and nine year-olds. It was now as respectable for us to play as baseball, bowling and tennis.

Al told me a few days after my beaning, "Wars better than baseball. What the hell does baseball teach you? Does it teach you to duck?"

The next two or three skirmishes proved to be almost on the verge of lethal. Meat and Bingo thought they had to find a way to make sure we didn't have to stop our games early because someone need to pay a friendly visit to the emergency room.

Who knew that Wayne would almost heave up a lung when he inhaled the yellowish dust that covered these monstrous ragweed plants. To him they were no different than stepping on a cobra.

From that day on; wearing a bandana or other rag around our faces was mandatory. The hills resembled more a young group of western outlaws then the true commandos we were.

When acting out amongst ourselves we always took the dirt of the roots. We'd bang them against the bottoms of our shoes or slap them against the ground a few times. If you weren't careful you could inadvertently leave a stone in amongst the root fibers. We wanted to have fun; not maim each other. Especially after that incident with Frank.

I can say I'm one of the few that can attest to the fact that in Nineteen Sixty-Eight the hills were certainly alive. They sure as hell weren't alive with the sound of music; it was more the sound of pain after you'd get hit in the bare arm or back with a dirty, pointed, flying Whomba.

Our strict definition as to what constituted a Whomba was simple. Meat and Mark made the first and final description and we all accepted it; right there and then.

Meat explained, "The stalk part cannot be longer than a foot or foot and a half. We start measuring from where the root joins the base of the green stalk to the end of the stalk. The root part is not calculated in the length. Anything hanging on the roots is not considered part of the plant. No stones or pieces of glass can be attached."

He even stressed it would be better if we beat the root-ball on the ground or shook them every time to prevent another, what he termed; "Schultzie or Swastika Incident".

As is the trouble with all weapons of mass destruction; you've got to tell your friends about them. Out of normal friendly bar conversation, with some of the fellows from the town next door, a few guys heard about our new organic projectiles. Seemed funny though, how after they were enlightened to the new world of the whomba; they started getting more and more distant.

One day they'd be friendly toward us and the next it was as if they hated our guts. For weeks I couldn't understand why. When a few of them saw me fishing along the border they didn't come over and shoot the breeze like usual. They weren't mean to me either. Could have been they didn't look at me as a threat. Could have been they knew who my father and grandfather were and the connections they had.

I did find out a minor fact from Meat and Al a short time before the battle, which could have had some bearing as to why these guys over the border didn't like us too much.

Al and Meat had gotten a little wasted one night and went over to the Duncan Donut by Dahnert's Lake. Coming upon two girls they had never met before they did what they always did; they ask them to go for a ride. Al said the ride didn't last all that long.

Meat added after the girls had a little to drink they thanked them with a little mouth service. When they took them back to the lake their boyfriends were waiting for them. Al said he could understand why they were a little pissed-off.

This small and insignificant act on their part mushroomed much like the Cuban Missile Crisis into a larger issue. Al and Meat dared to enter a foreign territory in search of something to cure the munchies. And managed to stumble upon another form of booty; sixteen year-old booty to be more specific.

Al had a very compelling argument. He told all of us on the bench the other night they didn't want to keep those girls; they just wanted to borrow them. Mike and Wayne seemed to be relieved the guys over in the other town never heard of Al's retort.

Here we were, just like in the White House, forced into a battle not of our making. Well, maybe it was of Al's and Meat's making, but not the rest of us. The other eight of us were no different than the other members of NATO. We had no choice but to join in.

We all couldn't believe how it all escalated. That water had long past under the Route 46 bridge and over the Dundee dam. It had made its way now to the Atlantic. The Passaic might have been polluted, but the water still managed to get to the sea.

# Chapter 9: Wednesday

One o'clock took forever to finally arrive on this sultry Wednesday afternoon in the last week of July. I was so used to working side by side with the five gentlemen that came up north every year from Puerto Rico that I hadn't yet realized they were one by one starting for the shade.

Joe, the foreman, rolled up on his Sixty-Three Ford 4000 wondering why the three of us remaining had not thrown in the towel. He was right; the humidity was too overpowering.

I had a totally stupid idea in my head. I actually thought if they could take the heat on an island near the equator, then they'd sure be able to stand a little heat in Jersey. Not quite so. Our humidity was actually something they'd write home about to their families; who they wouldn't see again until September.

I always thought it was strange that they would come so far and work so hard, when people over the river wouldn't even walk five blocks to a job. Always figured the reason was they were too proud to crawl for a handout.

When I walked to the back door I hesitated for a moment wondering if the pool temperature would be bearable. Some days in July the only way you could tell you were in the pool was by feeling the water against your skin. You sure couldn't tell by the temperature; there were many times the air was actually cooler. This afternoon would be fine for a swim. It wouldn't be a cold one; maybe not even a cool one.

My brother had been playing ball the whole time I was sweating my ass off pulling scallions. He never had a real desire to work and if he ever did he'd wait a few minutes until the feeling past.

Of course he was always going through my wallet looking for cash. Wouldn't you? It was easy to find. If it wasn't in my jeans on the chair, it was in the top drawer of my dresser. You can't wear a wallet doing farm work; it gets in the way or it'll just get lost. He loved it when I worked.

The cycle would go on and on; never broken. I'd work, I'd get paid, I'd put the money in my wallet and then he'd liberate it. My parents always had the attitude that if he was going to get killed in Nam in a few years, he might as well enjoy his time until then.

They were more in tune with the reality of day to day life than I was. I dare anyone to tell me they wouldn't be doing what the Sixties were famous for if they knew soon after senior ball they'd be dancing in a rice paddy.

I was floating in the pool when he came home around four. Nothing new, he stripped down right there by the ladder and got in with his underpants on. He couldn't give a crap if the neighbors saw him like that. I guess he was right. After all, they had seen him drunk before and this was a tamer, more disciplined situation.

Last week we had finished playing ball on another scorcher and he decided he couldn't wait the five minutes until we got home to take a dip. He went across the street to the hotel and jumped in their pool with his shirt and shorts on. Of course they called the police. And no; he didn't get in trouble.

If it were any other kid they might have had a better chance of at least some kind of reprimand. Everyone knows how the police take care of their own. Here is a kid jumping into a hotel pool in the middle of the afternoon with his clothes on. Shouldn't the officer at least talk to the boy? Exactly; the officer did.

He came over to my brother, who was now sitting on a swing next to me with a puddle on the ground underneath him.

He calmly asked, "How you boys doing today? Gary I see you're really sweating. Maybe you should go home and jump in your own pool."

That was it; end of conversation.

We got off the swings and started for home. We were about a hundred yards from the house when he asked, "Think I should say anything to Pop?"

I didn't bother to answer. He knew damn well that Pop already was fully aware of what happened. I would even wager, when that call came in to the police station, our father was already betting with his officers on which one of his sons it was.

If you hadn't had the opportunity of growing up in the Stone Age it would be hard for me to explain to you, who never had a "real" telephone, how one of those things operated. I'll try to give you a quick lowdown of why the Sixties phone was loved and hated at the same time.

Our house had four phones, which was unusual back then. Most homes had one in the kitchen, hanging on the wall. Maybe there would be a second in the master bedroom. The biggest problem back then was AT&T would dial your house and check how many phones rang inside. They charged by how many phones you had. People that were lucky enough to have a friend in the communications business would learn how to disconnect the bell; therefore disconnecting the bill that went with it.

A typical day back then would be just like that Wednesday afternoon when we left the pool to go inside. Our mother was on the phone when we entered the house and she was still talking when we had taken our showers and gotten dressed.

There was at least twenty to thirty minutes right there where all communication would come to a standstill. No other phone in the house, like today, to ring its little heart out. No, when someone else was on the line; you weren't.

You think that was bad; wait until I tell you about the privacy part. There was none. It was zero; zilch. The phone was bolted to the damn kitchen wall with a ten foot cord. How far away from the metropolis of your parents can you get with ten feet?

That son-of-a-bitch was so stretched by my brother and me there was hardly any recoil left in the thing. Even if you were trying to hold a conversation with God, it was loud and clear for everyone else around to hear. And yes, they only heard one side; your side. Speaking of God; I did thank him a lot back then for having phones all over the house.

Five o'clock was center stage and my mother finally hung the thing up. My brother grabbed it before someone else called us and called to the house across the street.

Al answered and they briefly discussed dinner plans. We were having pork chops, baked potatoes and a salad in twenty minutes. His mom was making meatloaf, mac and cheese and string beans at six.

Gooch slapped the phone down, after maybe two minutes total, announcing to my mother the Rileys were coming over to join us for dinner. We, of course, had to be done eating by six so we could then go over to their house for another entre'.

We pulled that shit all the time. It was surprising none of us were overweight. I guess it's hard to get fat when you're always active; sports, work, and walking everywhere.

Back then we didn't have the luxury of holding onto a phone until your ear got gangrene. With having to share only one line and no privacy; all our conversations were done face to face.

Maybe that's why kids today are so easily bullshitted and lied to. They don't know how to read another person's facial expressions. They have no clue whatsoever that the rain they feel on their back isn't actually coming from a cloud.

The one, and only one, great thing about having only one line of communication coming into your house at that time was being able to sometimes run interference. One example would be if the school called because you had decided to do something more exciting that day.

They called the house in those days; not your mother's cell. My brother and I were always appreciative of our grandmother on those mornings. Grandma's standard answer was always we were home and in bed. She never slipped up and acted like she didn't know we had skipped. She was a pro when it came to covering our asses.

The four of us sat through a half hour dinner at my house and then another half hour over at the Riley's house. We talked about all the safe and usual subjects. Nothing that had to do with what was really going on.

I could just see it now. Mrs. Riley would have gone ballistic if she had any idea her son Alan was working on setting me up with this seventeen year old.

We had met her at a party last weekend, and I was afraid to call her. I still wasn't sure if she knew my age or not. Al had told her I was seventeen. It's true; great friends are hard to find.

Right at the time we were leaving Gary grabbed the phone and called the D'Amico's house to inform them we were heading over to the school. If he didn't remind Wayne to bring a glove it was more than certain he'd forget one.

As I had expressed earlier about the phone always in use; he didn't always get his reminder call. Then he'd bitch for an hour that somebody should have told him we were playing ball. He really didn't care if we played or not; he had other things on his mind.

Six-thirty on the dusty dirt field was somewhat OK. We played on the east side of the building so at least home plate and most of the pitcher's mount was shaded. I was over the six foot mark, so it took until after seven for my eyes to be glare free if I was pitching. It was shaded when the ball left my hand, but if they hit a liner to my left the setting sun would almost guarantee I'd miss it. That was probably the only disadvantage of being tall.

On July Fourth, the Catholic Church had their carnival for five days. We all went together; all ten of us. Some of the gambling stands had an age limit. I was at least six foot, so they figured I was legal to play.

The wheel gave out a prize I think would be frowned upon today; cigarettes. You could win packs or cartons. Because I always liked this type of gambling, I think it was the sound the spokes made, I put a dime down.

The grungy man didn't say a word and when "eighteen" hit he gave me my choice. Of course in those days it was only Marlboro. In less than ten minutes I had two cartons.

The older guys, Al and Meat, were selling the cigarettes to the people in the crowd at a discount. When I had amassed a winning of nine cartoons, only because the other guys kept giving me more dimes, the shit running the thing said I was too young to collect.

We were taught back in the Sixties not to argue with adults. My brother didn't say a word. He calmly found a police officer on duty and explained how the carney took my money and then wouldn't fork over the goods.

Sure, we knew this man; he worked for our dad. He instructed the Marlboro man on the etiquette of gambling and I left with my nine cartons plus one extra. We sold every pack within thirty minutes; everyone smoked in the Sixties.

The advantages to being tall are endless. I was even granted admission to some of the bars in the area. I would squeeze myself between the older guys and act like I was supposed to be there.

On one occasion, when we went to the movies, they let me in and told my brother he wasn't old enough. He was shy of five foot ten and about to go ape-shit; until the girl let him in after Al put up a dollar tip.

That's one thing that was true in the years B. C. and will be true a million years from now. It doesn't matter how old you are if you're tall and have muscles. People will give you their unspoken respect; especially if there's a war on the horizon.

In that case they'll yell it off the rooftops they need your help. Yeah, the battle due to arrive on the weekend would be one man less if it weren't for the fact I was raised on fish and yogurt. The hard worked probably helped to add an inch or two also.

The sun had drifted lower, giving us all a reason to stop the game. It was so damn muggy. I guess by this time of the summer we were somehow used to the heat, but the swampy East Coast air was another matter. You never got used to it.

By nine o'clock on the days we played ball our legs, from the knee down, would have streaks of mud running down to our sneakers. The dust would cling to our legs like a magnet.

We'd use the outside water fountain the school left on to rinse as best we could. Even if you got your leg a little clean, you still had to tolerate the squeak sound your sneakers made from the water.

This night our company bench was occupied, so the troop gathered around the swings. Problem with being so close to the lights was they drew the mosquitoes. It was tolerable and where else were we to go?

Usually by nine-thirty the benches were always under our jurisdiction. Ten to fifteen more to go and they'd be on their way home. I got the impression the talk of battle would wait until the benches were regained. After all, one catastrophe at a time.

Mark was like a pig in shit. He had waited all too long to get his seat. He likes to sit on the backrest and put his feet down on the seat. It was actually a good idea; this left room by his feet for one more to sit.

He was sure the group would want to get down to business as soon as possible. He kept thinking to himself, "Tonight is Wednesday. That leaves two more days. Just two."

I liked to listen to what all the guys were saying, yet at the same time I knew I didn't have to pay attention to the details. Al, Mike and Meat wouldn't have me more than six inches from where they were during the invasion. They always liked me covering one of their flanks; be it everything from snowball fights to tug-o-wars.

Maybe it was the way I lit the M-80s while Mike threw them or when we happened upon something around town we could use. Al would ask if I could handle another twenty pounds. I was versatile to them; fast, accurate and able to lift stuff.

Wayne was swaying, still loosening the muscles in his legs, waiting for his brother and Meat to get perched, "Do we have a plan or don't we? What the hell are we waiting for?"

Schultz looked over toward Wayne, "What is it; around sixty hours?"

Gary was digging in his bag, trying to grab hold of a pint, "Yeah Meat. What gives?"

Bingo shrugged his shoulders, as if to say, "Don't look at me."

Then with the spring of a jaguar; Meat was standing, "OK assholes. I was looking over this book about war my dad has. Seems some gook wrote it a couple of thousand years ago. It's all about how to prepare and win a war. Pretty nifty stuff. Tomorrow I'll draw us a map and sort of a plan. Then tomorrow night we'll add the details."

Wayne asked the magic question he and his brother already knew the answer too; "So, is the battleground the hills?"

Al nodded and Bingo piped out, "You bet. That's what Sal and I discussed at work today."

Bingo worked at the Two Guys Department Store which sat well in the middle of the opposing town. He was really a good friend of this guy he worked with, but when allegiances called you had to pick your side. Which, more often than not, was determined by where you lived; not by how you thought. Kind of similar to that North-South thing about a hundred years earlier.

Mike turned to Schultz; who was taking a sip from a Rheingold. Which they rightly claimed to be an extra dry lager beer - not sweet.

Mike spoke as a commander, "Hey Schultzie, this is where you come in. You should be the expert; after all."

We all got the message at the same time. He was right about that; Schultz should be the expert on the weaponry pertaining to the hills.

It hadn't been a month since a few of the guys were coming back from the river when they decided to cut through the hills. They sat down in one of the small depressions deciding to take a small pot break before continuing home.

I guess Gooch had maybe puffed a little too much when he decided to pull one of the ten foot weeds out of the earth. He proceeded to break the bottom of the plant off about an inch from where it had gone into the ground. This left him holding a stub of almost one inch stalk and at least a foot and a half of dirt encrusted root.

When Schultz wouldn't hand the doobie over fast enough, my brother hurled that dirty root at him. The description from the others there was it acted more like a balanced Bowie knife than a root.

This clump of topsoil hid a small, but sharp piece of glass imbedded within the rock-hard cellulose root. It hit Schultz right between the eyes and up about a half inch.

When he took the Band-Aid off after about a week we could all see this was no minor scrape. One inch over either way and he wouldn't have had such good luck. Anyway, that was the birth of another weapon of the whomba variety that would live from then on in infamy. If only known to less than a dozen people on planet earth.

History teaches us that you can make a weapon out of anything. Even water; if you use it to kill someone. So in the true spirit of war; did this dirt-encrusted root serve as a weapon; as a whomba? Yes it did! Sort of.

Now, in the year Nineteen Hundred and Sixty-Eight, another new herbaceous weapon had emerged right alongside the A-Bomb, the H-Bomb and standard whomba. This new weapon would from this day on be known as the "Whomroot".

Although the Gantner Convention would soon rule it an illegal weapon; due to its cruel and unusual side-effects; similar to what happened with the mustard gasses of WWI.

The change in status occurred within hours after the Band-Aid was removed for good and Schultzie's mom saw the residual development.

When the scar, which was formally called "The Swastika", became apparent; it was voted by all that such a weapon should never again be unleashed against another human. Or animal; for that matter.

We didn't hesitate to vote this newly discovered horticultural ordinance out of our realm of weaponry; due to its everlasting effects on a fellow soldier.

After all; we were all Americans. Sure we loved to fight. We lived to fight. But when you're fighting brother versus brother, as in our American Civil War, you don't want to kill or disfigure them for life; do you?

# Chapter 10: Thursday

Meat was the first of the guys with a car to pull in by the teachers' parking area. Our game was still going on and from the position of the sun it looked like we had a good thirty to forty-five minutes left of good light.

The heat wasn't as bad as the days before, so we all decided to play on. When Bingo ripped into a spot two places over from Meat's the car swayed three times. He must have been doing thirty when he entered the lot.

Meat stood where he was, waiting for Bingo to catch up to him before he continued toward the ball field. We could see Bingo had a can in his hand, which was usually a beer, surrounded by one of those fake "Orange Crash" labels.

Not one person in the game moved, which gave them the signal we'd be playing until dark. The weather was too nice to stop. Could have also been the game was tied at six all.

After the fountain we made our way to the bench where we were greeted by a smile and a notepad full of notes and drawings. We could all tell Meat had spent hours devising his plan of action; actually our plan of action.

He had a separate sheet with everyone's name at the top, which he methodically handed out right off the bat. He told us the other night he'd make maps and a few notes; he did just that.

He made personal maps and notes for each one of us.

I remember Gooch laughing, "Good thing I don't have a damn draft card yet. This looks serious."

Schultz was the only one actually laughing out loud. He was looking at everyone else's papers, "Shit. How come I'm the only one on all the maps? Everybody will know where I am, but I won't know where they are?"

Meat smiled, "Exactly Schultz. You are the Ace-in-the-hole. If we get slammed; it'll be up to you."

Schultz couldn't help himself, "Yeah. They'll be calling me Meat next. Dead meat."

Mark hadn't looked at any of his handout yet; he was still trying to get his beer open after the pull-tab broke off. Pressing his house key on the little prong part finally worked. It sprayed both him and Gooch, but who cared? The golden liquid was now free and so was his undivided attention as to the matter at hand.

Holding his map out at arm's length, Meat told us we should look at our copies and see if they looked accurate. He and Mike swung by the site before work and didn't see any of the contractors around, so they pulled in as far as the gravel road went.

They were in one of their father's business vehicles, a yellow van. If they were questioned, they were going to say they were looking for work.

I was the first to notice the map was extremely accurate. I cut through the hills at least once a day either going to the sandwich shop or the river. The two of them made all the mounds and all the gullies look like a grade A military job.

After I told the guys the map looked perfect to me Gary piped in it was a good thing Meat read that book. Mike added he read some of it too, and what an education.

Meat was holding a paper he had written notes on and made the comment, "That book really stresses accuracy. I didn't do the map; Mike did. You know I can't draw for shit. Anyway, I know they're accurate. As accurate as the guy who wrote that book could do."

All ten of us were crowded together, except for the two foot section that we kept separated so the light would shine down on the papers. The second and only other page we had was the one with the notes.

Meat and Bingo had looked the book over and came up with steps to follow. Bingo wanted everyone to get their act together now, so we wouldn't be jerking around in the next ten minutes. I took this to mean we were now about to get serious.

Meat told us he had given the list of thirteen things that had to be done to Al. He wanted to compare what he came up with the list of things to do that he, Mike, and Bingo came up with.

This was going to be a joint effort. Speaking of which; it was right about then that Wayne did produce one and passed it around. It would help keep the minds concentrating and ideas flowing; so he said.

Bingo killed his third beer, maybe his forth, and made the announcement he would read the steps from the book titled "The Art of War".

He threw an empty at Schultz when he asked if it was written by Picasso or Rembrandt. Meat told him it was written by a Chinese General named Sun Tzu; over two thousand years ago.

Bingo started by saying he'd give the name of each step, then Mark would write down all the ideas everybody came up with. These would be compared with what Al and the others had already done. Last, they'd all work on which they thought would work out the best; and why.

Seemed like a plan to me. Seemed like these guys had already thought up a plan. One that might actually work too.

When Bingo said the first step was where you lay out your plans, do your planning and assessing, it only made Gary groan, "We're doing that now. Next."

Bingo looked at Meat and they both grinned, "Ok. Step two is where either Meat or I explain what's gonna happen. I talked to Sal this morning, so I'll say what we came up with. It's rather simple; we've decided on three rules.

Rule one is we use the standard whomba as we all know it. No spears, rocks, dirt-bombs or BB guns. Just whombas. Bang' em real good and get the rocks and sticks out.

Rule two is no piling-on. If you see a guy get hit in the head, don't go crazy winging more at him. If you do and get caught you're out.

Rule three is a chest or back hit and you're dead. It's the usual for arms and legs. No face or head shots. We don't want anybody going blind or getting Schultzied."

Wayne lit a fresh one, which gave Bingo pause to do the honors.

Al looked at Mike and stated, almost as if asking, "One hour?"

Mike was nodding while looking at his brother and Bingo, "Yup. Then we do the count."

Meat added after a puff and a swallow, "It's ten against ten. It may be over in fifteen minutes if we're lucky. Don't forget, no head shots."

Mark held his paper up so we all could see that the first two steps had no notes attached. Bingo took that as a hint to move on.

"Step three is planning our offensive. We know we'll be on the north side, so that's where your maps come in. Meat and Al thought it be best to save that for last.

So then there's step four; this is our positioning. The map has each one of our spots marked. Tomorrow night we'll go over there around ten or so to make sure it still looks the same. They won't be back Saturday.

Step five is strategy and directing of our forces. This is where Al will be in command. Tomorrow night while we're over there he'll have all of us in position and ready to go.

Then we have our plan of attack. Right now he's thinking it may be good to focus on one corner and move behind them. If we can do that it'll be over in five.

Step six is finding the enemy's weakness. It has to do with illusion and reality; this is where Schultzie comes in. If you look at your map you'll all see where Schultz is. He'll be on the hill back by the huge puddle. We checked this morning and it's still there.

Plus, he can see anyone coming from the other side. The water makes the roots easy to pull and he can start stockpiling as soon as the show starts.

They won't know he's there until it's been going on a while. Then Schultzie, you go into action. You whip those mothers off in every direction while we try to take the farm side and get two of us behind them. Shit, maybe even three.

Step seven is engaging the other side. This we don't have to worry about because we don't plan on getting that close. Next is eight.

The eighth one is about being flexible. If we get somebody out in the first five that changes everything. We have to show them where we are at the onset and for maybe five minutes at the most.

On the map I have your start position; your fire position will be somewhere else. Check tomorrow night where your best reload spot is. That's where you want to be. Mark did you get that?"

Mark was trying to keep up. The first steps had nothing, but he was making up for that now.

As soon as he put the pen down he asked, "Being flexible may want us to check out the positions near us tomorrow. If one of us gets taken out we may want to move over to his location. You think we should check out the other side too? See where they may want to move as a second choice."

Al spoke right up, "I'm with you on that. We want to see where they may want to shift to. You know we'll all be starting behind a hill, but sometimes that still leaves you open. Damn rockets are what got me the last time."

Gooch laughed, "Gary and I creamed you good. Hey, we should do that again. Put two; better yet, three on one hill. If we do a mass bombing from the get-go we may be able to take out at least two; maybe three. This would open the side to crawl around."

Al told Mark, "We'll do groups of three. Yeah, we'll do a blitzkrieg. Damn thing worked on me."

I hadn't said anything so far but wondered. Then I asked Al, "Why don't we time the blitzkrieg after we shift. This way we'll have more ammo. And if we do it in thirty second intervals Schultz can back up a different group each time."

Mike looked at his brother, though he was speaking to Schultz, "Schultzie; you may be able to see when one of theirs gets killed and then tell us when to start bombing another target."

Schultz shook his head in agreement and Wayne supplied him with a rolled token of enthusiasm. After a slight cough, Schultz proclaimed, "I'll spike those mothers two at a time."

Bingo proceeded with step nine which had to do with marching or moving an army. Gooch informed us all the only place he'd be marching to was a shower after the battle and then Januk's.

Step ten was the terrain. We had all agreed earlier to scope out the place tomorrow night, so that was the end of step ten. Besides, we all knew the place from top to bottom. Only problem was that occasionally a bulldozer would take a hill or two and move them fifty yards or so.

When Bingo hit step eleven he started laughing, "This step has to do with how the army attacks in a certain terrain; how they navigated the field of battle. Think this guy's army ever fought a Whomba?"

His only words on this one seemed to consist of, "First you sit by your hill, then you crawl around on your stomach, then you hope not to run out of ammo, then you standup and wipe the shit off yourself, then you hope your side won and then you go home. Next step."

When he looked at Schultz we all could see he was about to start his usual, "Schultzie this one's for you.

Step twelve is about attacking with fire; rockets. These Chinese would light a kite on fire and sail it over the walls or use a rocket. You know they invented powder. Anyway, we can't use fire; any other ideas?"

Our Schultzie smiled as if he knew the deepest, darkest secret in the world, "I'll come up with something. Don't worry."

I worried. I'm sure some of the other guys worried too. That look of his always meant he was ready to strike; not now of course, but soon. If he came up with something it would certainly be beyond the realm of "Normal"; but within the rules of the game.

Meat could see Bingo was happy with the fire he had lit under Schultzie's ass. He, like everyone else, had not a clue what would come of this, but it would most likely be quite bazaar.

Bingo was enjoying the evening as he said, "Last is step thirteen; spies. I guess I'm the only one that can be considered for this job. I've worked with Sal for about two years and we're good friends. We're meeting at Januk's Saturday; win or lose. But he's as tight about his side as I've been about ours. So unless one of theirs defects before Saturday I'd say thirteen is still unlucky."

We all agreed the plan of action was perfect and by tomorrow night we'd surely have all are ducks in a row.

The streets surrounding the school were giving me the sign it was time to hit the road. Summer nights were often like that.

If the day was real hot there was very little traffic and movement until around six. Then it was as if everyone was out and about doing everything they should have done all day. Then by nine-thirty or ten it would get real quiet. Almost too quiet. If you listened hard you could hear the traffic from the far off highway.

On the walk home my brother asked Mike what would happen if the other side decided not to play. This made Mark laugh.

He smiled out, "It's a war. Of course they're gonna want to play. Everybody plays when there's a war."

Ok, I was the youngest, so I asked, "What the hell do you mean by that?"

Mark slowed down until he was right at my side. Mike and Al started to slow then also. When Wayne slowed it was a traffic jam. All at once the conglomerate that was about to cross the bridge was frozen in place. All huddled together like cows in February, waiting for Mark's explanation.

"It's simple. So I'll explain. War is a game. Do we all agree on that?"

Everyone nodded and no-one rebuked; so I took it war was a game.

"All guys like to play games. Even our government plays games. Some our president starts, and some the other countries start.

Take the Japanese and the Germans for instance. They started a game and the whole world wanted to play. Then Korea started a game and when our guys got bored they quit.

So it's not like you have to play. You can play when you want and go home when you want. Sometimes our team wins and sometimes the other team wins. Even Vietnam is really a game. If all the politicians didn't like to play so much we never would have sent our team over there to play."

I might have been the youngest at fourteen, though I didn't think I was the dumbest either. I made the comment, "So all these wars are no different than the Whomba? If the other team doesn't want to play all they have to do is not show up?"

Mark answered with the magic word, "Exactly!"

This had the herd moving along again on its way.

I needed to know more from a guy who did have his shit together when it came to current events; "So Mark. If we don't want a war or our government doesn't want to go to war; you're saying all we have to do is not show up? Has that ever happened?"

He stopped for a second, "Not show up? Are you nuts? They always show up. You'll see Saturday. I'm telling you; everybody loves to play. Everybody loves war. Even with all the guys we know getting killed over in Nam, their parents love the idea we're playing.

Can't you see how they went crazy when Kennedy got shot? They'll be talking about him forever; everybody knows how much he loved to play. Johnson loves to play too."

Al told me when Mark finished, "You have to look at the politicians as the owners of a football team. They pick who plays who and who gets to start or play second string.

They never have their relatives on the twenty yard line in the mud and snow; they're always in the club box. The poor bastards on the field get their heads cracked a couple of times and their bodies bruised for life, while the owner's get most of the green.

Just like all the other games; coaches or politicians get the big bucks and the players or John Q. Public gets the shaft.

The fans love it that way. We're Americans. We love war, mom and apple pie."

I was in bed that night thinking about those last phrases while listening to the British Rock station on FM. I noticed probably for the first time, in my short but expedient Jersey-mode life, that every other song was about peace or war.

Could it be possible that other people on this planet were thinking kind of what I was thinking, "Do we always have to be playing the same stupid game?"

Some fans or politicians will swear it's not the same old game. They'll print their ideas in every paper from the New York Times to the Los Angeles Times that the playing field is totally new. Or they'll take out a full page add to show how our new team has different equipment. Usually trying to explain something mundane and irrelevant like the difference between an American football and a football from Europe.

When Country Joe McDonald and the Fish came on the radio with the Fish Cheer, better known as "I Feel Like I'm Fixin' To Die"; I was glad to hear one of my favorites.

Waking up on Friday morning I did remember one funny thing about the last song I heard before falling asleep.

We had been playing the games over in Asia for some time now and yet that last song was saying we should try peace; not war. How can an American not be into the games; isn't that's what this country stands for?

Then again, it was the British Rock station; maybe it was a foreign band. Those people over there aren't as gung-ho as we are.

# Chapter 11: Friday

Julio had parked the tractor over by the washing shed waiting for me to finish spraying down the last of the radish boxes. The short-bed truck was about to leave for the market, giving me time to ride over the hill with him to see what the others wanted for lunch.

They always tried to break around eleven. Their day usually started around six-thirty and they would work til four. If it was a scorcher it was more like three.

Now with the truck turning out of the drive and the water hoses turned off, I heard the low rumble sound of a dozer. When I jumped on the wheel fender I pointed to the key as if asking Julio not to turn it yet.

It was a dozer; plain as day. I couldn't see if it were in the hills or working around one of the houses. The only thing I could think of was, "The maps? What about our maps?"

Riding up toward the roadway I turned and tried to see exactly where the sound was emanating from. For as hot and dry as it was that morning I was kind of shocked I couldn't even catch glimpse of a slight dust cloud. Nothing, not even the telltale puff of black smoke that would hover every minute or two above the moving yellow-orange beast.

Not paying attention to where we were going, it took me off guard that we were down by the hazelnut trees in what seemed a split second.

I jumped down with my pencil and piece of paper taking down what all the guys wanted. Friday was payday for them and me; mine would last until that Saturday night at least. The guys would always chip in on Friday and buy my lunch. This was always something special to me. I knew they were busting their asses in a foreign place just to make ends meet at home. I never ate as much as I could have.

Instead of taking my usual trek, down the farm road toward the river and then hanging a right to the Sub Base, I went across the bridge. Jumping the fence that was supposed to keep kids like me off the parkway land; I hurried toward the now growing roar.

It was all open land and I was on higher ground. The nearer I would get to the sound, the nearer I would be to the hills. Hopefully, the dozer was within the houses and not running rampant on our battlefield.

If it were after three in the afternoon I would have thought twice about walking right down the middle of their project. But I had a pass in my pocket. I had a lunch order that needed to be filled. If any of these guys was going to stop their machines and get down just to yell at me I had my ticket out.

I dared them to stop a fourteen year-old making a lunch-run. If these guys were going to be mad about anything, it was that they didn't have a kid to do a lunch run for them. I figured if they stopped me I'd just ask what they wanted me to pick up for them. I'm so accommodating at times; maybe they'll tip too.

The hills looked more and more untouched the closer I came toward them. Hitting the gravel roadway I could see and hear the dozer smoothing out the last yard of the development. I thought that even if they worked all day, they still wouldn't be ready for the topsoil until Monday.

Saved by the lack of motivation again. I'd watch these guys work sometimes and believe me when I say if the guys from the farm were working this project it would have been completed a good two months earlier. I did learn as I got older that "Time and Material" is as sacred as the Virgin Mary; especially the Time part.

The man on the dozer was sweating his ass off and the two guys walking around almost resembled the people I'd see on Canal Street in the City. Not one of them bothered to raise a chin or wave, so I walked up to the guy on the machine and made the sign of drinking.

He hit the kill-switch in an instant, "Hey boy, what can I do for you? You need water?"

I told him, as he climbed down dusting himself off, "I'm making a lunch run for the farmers over there; you want me to get you guys something? I'm heading to the Sub Base."

He didn't say "yes" or "no".

He reached his left hand in his pant pocket and pulled out a ten. Smiling and looking toward the other two men, "Here, get me a large Italian; with everything. And grab me two sodas; Pepsi or Coke. See what the other ones want, OK? Tell'm it's on me."

He jumped right back up in the seat. The roar and bellow of black smoke was my cue to get moving.

The other two ordered the same kinds of sub, though when they learned the other guy was buying they changed their drinks from one to two also.

The short time I walked over to the Base from there was spent trying to do the math and figure if there was enough left over for a tip. Not for the guy making the subs, for the guy delivering them.

I made it back to the farm by taking the direct route, after dropping the order off at the houses. I was in a much better mood walking back than I was walking down.

The hills were untouched, and they gave me a total of a buck tip. One of them asked if I'd be back around Monday. Shit yeah; for a buck I'll be back every day.

Working in the field by the hazelnut trees it was easy to watch the vehicles going by toward my house. I could tell it was around four-ten when Mrs. Riley went by and beeped the horn. That meant the gang would all be in their homes within the half-hour.

One thing good about the farm job was I didn't have to walk all the way back to the barn. I said my goodbyes and started across the field. I'd be home in two minutes; or less.

My brother handed me the phone as soon as I walked in the door, "Here, it's Al."

"Hey, what's doing?" I think he could tell by my voice I was tired; maybe even dirty.

"Just saw you walking home. Get changed and come on over. Steak and eggs; how about it?"

Be over in ten." I hung the phone on the wall and ran to the bathroom.

In the shower my brother wanted to know what the hurry was for. I told him Al's mom had some leftovers; fish. What the hell; he didn't need to know. He'd surely find out by dark anyway. I knew he wouldn't want to go over there for dinner. Gary and he had made plans to go drinking at Januk's as soon as Gary got home. He'd be out the door before I was.

During dinner I explained to Al how my day went with all the excitement of the hills. He was well aware of how nervous that roar of the dozer would have made me. He told me he'd been a little edgy ever since his alarm went off. He was always so cool; I couldn't imagine him even being bothered a little.

We were walking through the farm to the ball field when he uttered out, "I hope those bastards play fair. None of the usual shit."

I wanted to say something to the effect, "Play fair? I thought it was a war? Who the hell plays fair in a war?"

Does a fourteen year-old kid have to be the voice of reason when we're about to enter a battle? I hope the hell not. I kept my mouth shut and waited to hear what else he'd share.

"You know that tall skinny kid, the one that looks like he has worms, he brought a BB-gun last fall over to the falls. I was about to stick it up his ass when the cops showed and took the thing away from him. What an A-hole."

The way he said the statement in a matter-of-fact way made me start laughing. I had to turn to my left so he wouldn't think I was laughing at him.

Al was just like that. He wouldn't show any emotion about if he were mad or anything; then all hell would break out.

He watched this guy bulling Schultz one time and the guy went on and on calling him Schultzie in front of this group of girls. Al never said a word. He calmly walked over by the guy and took one swing. Down he went. Actually down and home. He never bothered Schultz again or anyone else for that matter.

He reminded me there wasn't a game this night because our brothers had decided to try to get into the local bar. Sure, the bar was around three or four miles away, but it was the closest establishment that would serve them; or me.

They always walked the distance; that's why they had to start right after dinner. If they were allowed in they would stay til around ten. This left them ample time to stop for something to eat on the slow walk home.

Cathy and Sophie were perched on the bench, which made our timing perfect. They were both in the sixteen to seventeen age range which Al had told me months ago was just right for us. He laughed when he told me he'd have to make sure he didn't make any mention of my age or grade in school.

They went to the Catholic school, so he always assumed they didn't know us that well. Little did we know in less than two hours' time we would both be educated to the topic of the night; they were well aware of who and how old we were.

When Sophie went to the trash can and returned with a Pepsi bottle to play a round of STB, it occurred to me my age wasn't that big of a no-go for them.

Al whispered to me when he thought they couldn't hear, "Told you. Nothing to worry about. They like you."

He must have been right; that bottle didn't stop for an hour.

The pole light was well lit in comparison to the darkness that was now overtaking the evening. Every member of the club was either on the bench or near it. The girls left at the first sign of dark. Al thought maybe it was all the other guys showing up. Anyway, as he stated, we had business to attend to.

Meat was asking if we should walk to the hills or all pile in the two cars that were available when the two Garys decided to enlighten the encampment.

It was a scene out of either an Abbott and Costello or a Laurel and Hardy movie. No matter which; it was a scene. The two Garys each had brought a six pack of the long-neck Buds.

I'll never forget Al asking if his brother got them from home. No, they didn't get them from home. They bought them over at Januk's and walked the three-plus miles with them. They were a little warm. Ok; they were hot, but they went down anyway.

The group consensus was now that beer was involved it would be better to walk. It wasn't that far, and we could all talk the way over. First thing Al, Meat and Mark did was compare all their notes about how to start the game. I, along with the others, walked a few feet behind hearing the discussion word for word.

Mark was hooked on the word that Al seemed to like as well; blitzkrieg.

Mike had to agree. He said something to the affect, "If it worked for the Germans, it should work for us."

He also said, "Three M-80s would do the trick. I'm sure that's all we'd need. Three well placed M-80s and the game would be ours."

I know he wanted the game to end as soon as possible. He had a steady that any one of us would have dropped everything for; including our pants. He only agreed to be in the game because Meat asked him. If his Diane had any idea of his involvement I'm sure he wouldn't be with us right now.

The hills were as untouched as I had seen them at lunchtime. We were confident they'd be fine the next morning because the construction workers always got paid on Friday. That meant they'd get drunk Friday night; no way they'd work on Saturday. It was the American way of doing business.

Wayne look at his brother, who was bigger and heavier than him, "Where should we go first?"

Mark was about to pass the first hill when he turned around, "Let's all find our spots before it gets too dark.

Check around for your ammo and which way you want to go during the attack."

Al was on the north side of his spot when he added, "Schultzie, stand on the top and let everyone see where you are."

Schultz had one of the best hills in the land; he had the Matterhorn. It wasn't the highest, that would be Mt. Everest; which was on the other side of the playing field. The Matterhorn may have been second in height, but it was wider across. He would have ample protection; plus a protective moat.

Schultz wasn't a very tall guy, yet he seemed big. It wasn't that he was fat or even overweight; he just looked bigger than he actually was. His crew-cut hair style was probably the shortest of all of us. He was always complaining his hair was sunburnt; the main reason for this could be he never wore a baseball cap.

Standing on his hill, his Matterhorn, instilled in me the notion we had already won. It was as if I was seeing a picture of tomorrow's battle at the very end.

Standing on the hill, in the glow from the parkway headlights, he looked more like one of those Nordic warriors, than a kid with the nickname "Schultz". I, to this day, wish we had taken a picture of him.

He stood at the very summit of that hill holding at least four whombas in each hand. He held all of them with the roots up. It was a hell of a sight. I remember Wayne saying something to the effect that all the enemy has to do is see him like that and they'll run.

Gary was positioned on Little Round Top and Gooch was right behind him on Big Round Top. The hills were average size. Little Round Top was slightly smaller; leaving room for Gooch to fire over Gary's head.

There was still a row of hills closer to the border. Meat and Al thought it would be better if they stuck the two of themselves kind of side by side. Meat said if they were the most likely to get killed in the first five minutes, we'd might as well have their two hills go at the same time. I guess it isn't necessary to elaborate on how vital and strategic their hills were; or really weren't.

Bingo was given his own average size hill to the far right of the field. His fortress, known as Beverly Hills, was called that due to a slight depression to the back of it. The way the dirt was piled around the base in the back it resembled a small couch.

He was a tall, kind of skinny kid, who would have rather spent the entire day sprawled out on the hard packed dirt. Yet we all knew he could do the job when we needed him. His job was to protect the front line and try to make the run around to the enemy's side. He knew he might be one of the first to get whombaed.

To the left of Bingo, and slightly to the front and right of Little Round Top was my station; my hill. Capitol Hill had its name for one good reason. It had the most abundant, biggest weeds on the planet.

This hill resembled more a tropical rain forest or what we pictured a marijuana field in Mexico to look like. I had been given instructions by Al and Mike, that my first job at the hill would be to start production of whombas, which would be used for our invasion around the right flank.

The hill just behind mine was where Mark was stationed; ready to follow Bingo and Al into the enemy's camp. This hill never had a name until this very night when Mike teased him about the battlefield being so close to his house. He kept on and on that while we were fighting Mark would be home eating and watching us from the back porch.

When Mike said he'd be sitting there eating pork chops Meat went wild.

He started pointing to the hill, "Perfect name. Perfect name. Mark's gonna sit atop Pork Chop Hill." Of course the name stuck; and we all went berserk.

The four hills that sat on the border were manned by the guys who would get the brunt of the battle. Wayne was all the way to the left on Bunker Hill. He was probably the most muscular and athletic of all of us.

He wasn't that big, but he could do flips off the diving board or climb a rope to the gym ceiling. He was a spider monkey in a t-shirt and shorts. Meat knew he could run around the hills and take cover somewhere else if he needed to.

Mike was on San Juan Hill just a few feet to Wayne's right. His was the second closest hill to the border and was in range of most of the enemy's hills. This could prove to be good for us or very bad for him. His only worry was how much dirt was going to be in his slightly long blonde hair.

He didn't mind getting dirty; it was just a pain in the ass to wash out.

Cemetery Hill was named for being the one closest to the line. It was no more than eight yard from the closest enemy hill. Meat volunteered to take this one mostly because he didn't want the rest of us to fight or maybe panic. Eight yards isn't far if you're throwing a hand grenade. I was always under the impression a whomba is a sort of grenade; I think I'm right on this.

To Meat's right was Al atop Cavanal Hill. This hill in Oklahoma is the tallest hill in the world; it's one foot shy of a mountain. The guys named it Cavanal when we first started messing around the hills, but since then our hill has really shrunk down.

Mark thinks all the rain a month ago did a job on it. Al didn't seem to mind; he had a good view of the surroundings from the now shortened monster.

The way Al was walking around the base of the hill he reminded us all of a Vietnam protester marching. His long hair fell over his glasses and face as he looked down checking out tomorrow's terrain.

He just kept walking and walking; as if he had a purpose. I did actually think he most likely did; he was the one who would get everyone else to the other side. The more we watched; the more we all could tell he sure as hell had a purpose.

Meat and Al stayed on their hills while we all gathered in between the two of them. Meat started with a general plan of attack and Al explained how Mark and Bingo would pass by me getting weaponry on their way to join him and then cross over.

It all made good sense. It made even better sense when Meat said we should all now inspect the hills opposite our own. See what we were up against.

Schultz took the initiative to ask if we should start pulling all the weeds. Mark called him some obscene word and told us not to even leave too many footprints.

He did have a point. If we were going to win; we had to win fairly. After all, we are in America; the home of the brave. We can't cheat in a war, especially when both sides are Americans; can we?

Just like in the last battle fought on our own beloved homeland soil; didn't each side win? When in the South you see all the progression of new wealth and vitality in their cities. They even have a healthier tax-bracket than in the North. Yet, the history books say the North had won.

While in the North the major cities are barely hanging on and everyone can't wait to move to the South. Maybe nobody won; or maybe both sides won.

Yeah, I'm sure both sides must have won. Cause every war since the Revolution we've always won; even though I'm sure not every history book would say that either.

# Chapter 12: Saturday 8 a.m.

Walking into the kitchen, still somewhat groggy, I couldn't help but notice my brother had our baseball gloves sitting by the backdoor. It was as if he was already working on our alibi for the morning and I hadn't even woken up yet. I would have been happier if he had made more coffee or better yet; started on breakfast.

He must have been on the phone while I was in the shower, due to the fact I never heard him talking to Gary or Al at all. If I were going over to the farm or the river I wouldn't have bothered washing until I got back. Usually I just put my head in the sink and washed my hair. What's the use; you're gonna be all sweaty and dirty in ten minutes anyway.

Now Al, on the other hand, would take a shower on the way to his appointment to get tarred and feathered. If only they had some kind of sanitizer you could get in a bottle and wipe it all over your hands. He'd buy this stuff by the case.

My brother had stayed out later than I and informed me the plan was to meet at the hills by a quarter til nine. He kind of laughed when he said the "Meet" word. I got his drift on that one.

With four of the guys coming up the hill and two across the street, with us included, that was already eight. Only the D'Amicos were left to be added. And we had to pass behind their house on the way down.

After a rather larger than normal breakfast we started on our way. We were going across the street and wait with the

Rileys for the others. Gooch was actually wondering if they had any donuts or coffee still left.

I was starting to think he planned on taking a few items down to the battlefield to snack on during the fracas. I mean he was on Big Round Top, but hell; did he think he'd be able to eat during all that was going on?

Al was watching the street for the others more intensely than the dog was. Maybe that was because my brother did find the donuts and was again sitting down to another light breakfast.

Gary was drinking coffee right there next to him, as if they had all morning. Finally Al turned around and announced our party was right out the front door. So off we went; sure, we all had coffee and some kind of food in our hands.

The Sixties would be considered strange years to kids today when it came to breakfast foods. Eggs were just the starters. Always accompanied by skillet-browned potatoes and onions, sausage, bacon or ham, juices, breads and cereal.

Our fathers fought in overseas wars where some mornings they were served nothing for breakfast, or lunch; or dinner. A diet of stale cigarettes and foreign plants was a thing of the past; that would stay in the past. Post-War food was to be good food, substantial healthy food and plenty of it.

Dropping a frozen waffle, pancake, donut or something like two pieces of cardboard with one-millionth of an ounce of artificial fruit between them would not suffice. Men of the

Sixties didn't fight the Germans and the Asians just to come
back home and wake up every morning to the smell of
toaster cooked recycled newspapers.

Far from it; they made sure their children's friends always
had food too. I guess once you've been without you really
do appreciate what you have.

We eight slowly marched on down the grassy strip
between the houses and the parkway. We couldn't go all
that fast; we were all still eating.

Mike laughed it was a good thing we didn't have to carry
weapons. When I asked why, he said with a mouthful, "My
hands are full now. Here, hold my coffee a minute. You
want a Snickers or Milky Way?"

Nobody else laughed; their mouths were full.

Mark and Wayne were waiting on their side of the fence.
Mark, of course, had to ask, "Hey, before we climb over does
anyone want to use the bathroom or get anything to eat?
Mom's worried you may be hungry."

See, just what I was talking about. Never failed. Wayne
could see we were all doing fine and was the first one over. I
held his thermos of cold water and what was left of a dozen
Dunkins while he scaled over to our side. He just smiled and
asked if anyone needed a donut.

Bingo looked at his watch as we approached the first hill,
then looked toward the river. He could see Sal Manis and his
army sitting on a pile of pavers over by the light blue house.
He told us to hang back while he, Meat and Al went to
powwow. They seemed to be over there a long time; more
than ten minutes.

We all got to see what the holdup was as soon as they were in view. Sal's guys had brought pizza from the night before. Hell, all three of them were eating a slice and Al was carrying a box back to us.

Mike asked his brother if he should run some of his candy bars over to their side. Meat shook his head negatively; seemed they brought all kind of stuff. Al said it looked like they were going to have a picnic over there.

Bingo synced his watch with Sal's and the start time was in twelve minutes. Each one of us made way for our hill except for Schultz; he was already there. The rest of us couldn't help but see what he was doing. He pulled two plants and had the roots stuck in the dirty, stinky, green water.

You couldn't wipe that grim off his face with a damn crowbar. We all knew what he was going to do. I thanked God right then for him being on "our" side.

Bingo let out a warning that we had eight minutes to go. He was a good looking guy who would have been our commander if the newspapers showed to cover the war. He just had that "all together" look. The look we'd see on the evening news during all the major battles in Vietnam.

Back then some of us actually thought those guys lived the news first hand. It wasn't until we were a few years older that we realized all they really had to do was read a cue-card and look exceptionally handsome.

The countdown to the action had started and from my vantage point it didn't look any different than a half hour earlier. I mean it was crazy; everyone on our side was still eating and drinking. Almost as if they were home sitting in their backyards waiting for Mom or Dad to fire the grill and get the dogs out. I'm not saying I was nervous; maybe just hyper waiting for the show to start.

Trying to remember exactly how many times I had joined in the games in the past took my mind off my present predicament for about two minutes. I couldn't get the notion out of my skull that this was more than a regular exercise in military awareness.

I turned to look at my brother, who was behind me and to my left, trying to see if he showed any signs of apprehension. It was clear he didn't. If he did, he hid it very well.

He and Gary were doing what they always did. They were sitting on the ground between the two hills bullshitting and eating.

It was either A or B. A; they had no clue where they were and what was about to start. Or B; they knew and just didn't give a damn. I was more inclined to go with B; Al would have seconded me on this I'm sure.

Mark was directly behind me, digging in as if the Russians were coming and not the guys from the neighboring town. I could see the determined expression in his face. He was astutely aware of the impending situation and was getting prepared.

He was one of the few guys I had ever known like that. He could laugh and horse around as much as anyone, but when you needed someone serious to handle a major situation; he was your man. Besides; he did have a good

head on his shoulders. He was often accused of thinking;
before he acted. Unlike most of us.

Scanning the front row of hills I could now understand
why Meat and Al had set it up that way. The defensive line
of Wayne, Mike, Meat and Al was a certain rival to Patton's
front offensive force. They would certainly hold back any
invasion and would be more than capable to progress
forward when the time should arise.

These guys were always making the statement that
Schultz was crazy the way he took all the risks all the time.
Now they were taking all the risks. The difference was I, and
everyone else behind them, knew they weren't crazy. They
were far from crazy; they had balls.

I watched Al as he inspected every weed on Cavanal Hill.
He hadn't pulled one out to start his war-chest; as I was sure
some of the others had already done. No, Al was too honest.
He wouldn't break any rule; not even in a war. He'd
probably make a great politician someday; that is if he'd
learn to lie more.

Sal knowing Al, though not as well as Bingo, could attest
that if our side should win it was an honest fight. The chance
of after-battle petitions of misconduct against our side
would be nil.

Al would demand that; along with Meat and Bingo.

Crawling around on my knees I tried to get a look in
Wayne's direction. I could see Mike squatting near his hill,
so I assumed he was in good shape. Mike had a way of
giving you a self-confidence boost almost every time he was

near. He had this positive outlook on everything; even things that went so terrible wrong.

Like the time he, Gooch and I tried to sail down the brook on a car top. What a freakin disaster. We got about four feet from shore and the damn top started sinking. Mike grabbed a low hanging tree limb and told me to swing to shore like in the Tarzan movies. I did as I was instructed and so did my brother. Somehow, someway; we all ended up on shore safe and dry.

I felt that same relaxing feeling I always had when he was around. The feeling that everything would turnout alright. He was a lot like his brother in that regard. Maybe that's why I never hesitated to get involved in anything they asked me to do.

I sat waiting for the games to begin knowing it wouldn't be that bad. How could it? The enemy might have been only thirty feet in front of me, but they had to get past Mike, Meat and Al first.

I could see that Al had moved to his left and was talking to Meat. Meat took off to his left to say something to his brother and he was right back to his position. Mike was on his was over to Wayne while Al hightailed it back between me and Bingo. They were relaying the news; the prewar surveillance.

Al's chest, from his neck down to his knees, was covered with dirt and the games haven't even begun. He crawled around the side of Cavanal Hill toward the enemy line and couldn't believe what he heard. Most of all the guys on the other team had amassed right along the border. Instead of taking the second and third rows of hills, as we did, they all moved forward.

Meat and he decided that our three front right hills would fall back to the hills just behind them. From the second row they would double up with Gary, me and Bingo and have a better chance of survival.

Wayne was stuck on Bunker, way to the left, because he couldn't drop back. Schultz was directly behind him on the Matterhorn; which was almost completely surrounded by a moat.

During their hasty prebattle discussion Al was certain Schultz could cover Wayne. Maybe even do more than cover; he could pass him those stinky wet whombas he'd been stockpiling. Al and Meat were so sure that Sal had made a massive blunder; they almost felt sorry for his side.

Al's orders were to throw high and short. Let their closeness be their worst enemy. He wanted all ten of us to concentrate our aim on the very front row of hills. He wanted our projectiles to come down on them like a pouring August rain.

Just before Al had returned to join Bingo he told Meat it may only last ten minutes. Meat was now alongside of me on Capitol Hill; the greenhouse of whomba jungle.

Al couldn't believe the guys across the line, the soldiers on the opposing side, chose to hold their ground behind the first line of hills. The main reason being there are only three hills on the border. The second row had four, Everest being one of them.

Mike had joined my brother Gooch at Little round Top and was waving to Meat to meet him right now in the middle. They talked for two seconds then Mike ran back up to his San Juan Hill.

Meat ran over to Al and in a flash they too went back to their original hills. I looked toward Bingo to see if he had any understanding as to what had just taken place. He shook his head, as if he were in the dark, just like me.

Bingo looked at his watch and gave me the thumbs up before sticking his head out of the weeds like a spring woodchuck in a field of alfalfa.

He bellowed his order, "It's show time. OK Sal?"

We all heard the yell back, "OK, Good luck." And the games began.

Our side had fought this battle before and had somewhat of a good idea of how the first minute of the action would go. We knew to use the weeds as a shelter at first.

We had fought our little battles in the past weeks; though with only three or four on a side. But we did learn the basics of fighting a whomba scrap. Unlike our opponent; who we really didn't know if they had even practiced this type of fighting and maneuvering on this field or any another.

The sky started to fall within seconds of Sal's words "Good luck".

Their timing was as if they had done what we usually did. We'd start breaking stalks the minute we sat next to out hill. It was kind of illegal to start before the actual blastoff time, but we all did it.

I could tell, and so could everyone else on my side, that the way they were throwing them; they'd be out of their stockpiles in no time at all.

Schultz ran over to Gary and said something real quick and then went back to his Matterhorn. He hadn't thrown one weed. I hadn't either and I wasn't about to stick my head out to see what everyone else was doing.

Gary ran over to me and said that Mike, Meat and Al went back up front just to let them think they were still there. They each threw one or two and were on their way back. It was now time to cover their retreat.

I motioned to Bingo that the guys were falling back. He could see Mark had been joined by my brother and the two were running to join him.

Schultz let out a yell that would have sent Godzilla back to his mother's arms. Gary, Bingo, Gooch, Mark and I took that as our "Rebel Yell". I had at least twenty projectiles waiting to go, and the guys started chucking like the natives in a Johnny Weissmuller movie.

Mark could throw a football like a pro and he could throw a whomba even further. We must have let at least fifteen fly in the first thirty seconds. By the time Mike, Meat and Al were next to me and Bingo, it was a Grand Central Station of whombas.

I kept pulling the weeds and snapping the stalks; while the other guys readied, aimed and fired. During our onslaught Al told us in another couple of minutes Sal's guys will have probably denuded the three forward hills.

He went on telling us that they had to go back to the front, so they'd throw their whombas at the first hills. Al was sure with eight of their guys up so close to the line they'd soon run out of weeds to hide behind.

That was one of the first things we learned when we started to play this game. If you take all the weeds out you'll lose your cover. These ten to fifteen foot giants make a great wall to hide behind. I learned on the first day from Mike to just pull every fifth weed. If not, your ass will be sticking out and it won't be long before it will get whombaed.

Gary threw a dirt-bomb my way to get my attention and I in turn threw it at Bingo. Gary didn't say a word, he didn't have to; he just pointed toward the Matterhorn.

He was mouthing the word "Schultzie" when the yell took over the battlefield again. We could see the slime dripping from the green muck soaked roots of the whombas. It was the grossest, foul smelling, rank thing you could imagine.

Wayne was left alone now on the front line for a good five minutes and taking all the heat. The other side had finally realized that the best way to throw a whomba was straight up with a seventy to eighty degree arch. Tossing them straight ahead only hit the high weeds that we hid behind.

Schultz had watched Sal's crew bombard Wayne long enough; he could no longer be a bystander.

Three in each hand and all six went up at one time. It was unbelievable that he had such control over where they were going. From where I was I could see that each group of three traveled to their destinations as a single clump.

There was nothing in the rules that said you couldn't throw more than one at a time. We just never did it. I guess none of us had the coordination to get one where we wanted it all the time; let alone three from each hand.

I wasn't the first to hear the words. "Shit" "This stinks" "What the Faaa?" "I'm out." "Me too." "What the hell is this shit?"

Schultzie!" "Schultzie!" "Schultzie!" Echoed from where Al, Meat and Bingo were.

He didn't even look their way. He scurried down the side of his hill, grabbed more whombas, dipped them in that green slime and ran around to the front to hurl again.

He had not a clue; he couldn't see from where he was way to the left. Three of the enemy had started walking down toward the houses. Three were KIAed in the first round of his blooper madness.

Gooch was the first to realize Schultz had made the way for us to counterattack. He yelled to Schultz first, "Schultzie! Khong Xau! Khong Xau! Don't stop!"

Then he turned toward my way, "Move forward, move forward."

Mike went back to San Juan to join Wayne, while Mark and Meat went up to Cemetery. Meat yelled back for Al to take Cavanal and Gooch joined him. Al was dead on with his dire prediction of what they might have done to those front hills.

Their front line no longer resembled a plush green of jungle brush. The barren hills just on the other side of the border looked as if they had never been home to a single weed.

The hills on our side still resembled a tropical rain forest; they were untouched. The three hills opposite them looked like the landscape of Mars.

They had to either move forward or move backward. To this day I don't know why they retreated. Maybe they thought we'd have no ammo if we crossed the front line. Stupid assumption; we had all the ammo we needed. We hadn't touched our first row of hills yet.

We still had our full regimen of ten, while they were down to seven; or maybe even less. Wayne was taking a breather for the first time since the battle started. He dropped back to aide Schultz in the soaking of the whombas.

He laughed later that he could tell they were flying overhead; each time some of that slime would rain down on him. He didn't mind if he stunk a little, as long as Schultzie kept him in the game.

# Chapter 13: Saturday 9:11 a.m.

As in all the previous battles I was in amongst these hills; the first ten minutes were no different. It was as if an entire action, that should have taken a good five or six hours, was simply condensed into a few hyper minutes.

I often wondered if it was like this on the real battlefield. Was time no longer time as we knew it? Did these type of actions follow their own laws of physics?

Hard to explain I guess unless you've experienced it firsthand. Maybe this is the mystery part of war; the part of the game that keeps bringing everyone back to play. I can't speak for the others, but I kind of liked it.

The morning leading up to the conflict was no different than any other. I can even say that the hour before didn't seem that unusual either. Truthfully, the five to ten minutes just before showtime did have me on edge, but once I looked around and saw my company I felt relaxed; more at ease.

I bet that's the way most of the soldiers would feel in a real battle. It wouldn't be so bad staring down the Japs as long as you had your friends on your left and right flanks; would it?

If these games teach a fourteen year-old anything it's the meaning of comradery. One learns you don't even have to like the guy next to you to respect him.

It's a game of sharing like no other. My fellow soldiers agree to share their skills and protection for my behalf; I in turn agree to share my abilities with them. A more elaborate form of one-hand-washes-the-other cannot be found anywhere else on earth.

Probably the most amazing attribute of the game is the passage of time. There is no consciousness of this at all. From start to finish, no matter what the span in time, there is only just that; a start and a finish.

The breaks that would occur in games such as baseball, basketball or football are nonexistent. From the initial spark of the word "GO" it moves at warp speed to an inevitable end.

How long to the end is irrelevant while the game commences. I guess if someone, say like a congressman or president, was watching from the sideline, he would occasionally notice a slackening in the playing. Although; even this fourteen year-old could assure them we, the players, never felt like we were slowing down.

I guess if our leaders in Washington ever wanted to experience the true virtues of war all they would have to do is don a helmet and join in the festivities. They would experience firsthand how time truly does fly when you're having fun. They might even forget to wave to their associates to pull them out of the game, because they're so involved.

This fast-paced action may sweep them away to a place they've never been; to an emotion they've never felt. There's nothing more than being in the game yourself to show your constituents how American you really are.

Or as they have mostly all done in the past; they can be generous and pass this highly sought after exhilarating experience to someone else. Why should they enjoy the games themselves and not share.

Isn't it better for all of us young Americans if we can have a shot at being in the games? Even if you can't qualify for the U. S. Olympic Team you can still make Uncle Sam's team.

In the slight lull. Actually it wasn't a lull on their side; they kept winging away while our guys moved about to the front. On the move forward I handed the guys at least six well-rooted whombas apiece.

Nothing can be worse than having to take the time to pull and break a weed when the sky above you is raining dirt and sticks. Experience told all the warriors on my side to never be caught unwhombarmed. I mean; if you crawl around a hill and the enemy has got you in his sights you're screwed. Unless of course you can give him a good whomba kiss.

The crawling around was starting to show more on Al, Mike and Meat than the rest of us. It hadn't gotten that sticky-hot yet, but with all the sweating and dust and dirt everywhere you can imagine.

Meat looked like one of those cinnamon donuts. He was evenly covered with the fine dark topsoil from head to toe; as if it were applied by a spray gun.

We always wore long pants in the war zone. I did notice earlier however, that two of Sal's friends had shorts on. That's one mistake I'm sure they'll never make again.

The enemy kept on with the barrage and it suddenly occurred to me that my teammates on the front line may just be sitting there waiting for them to pull the second most stupid trick of the game.

I pulled and cracked, pulled and cracked and pulled and cracked my ass off. When I had about twenty weapons I yelled for Mark and scrambled to meet him to deliver the ammo.

He was smiling the entire time. He told me how I had guessed it. Our front line was hanging low, while they kept on and on. Mark said the weeds were acting like a canopy and shielding them pretty good.

Mark turned toward Schultz, "No need for us to fire; look at Schultzie. He's killing them all by himself."

Poor Schultzie. He was covered with that green slime shit from his neck down. It was gruesome. We all agreed, even Sal's side, that how he put up with the smell was worth saying he won the War all by himself. He made the river water seem like aqua pura.

On his way back to Cemetery Hill to join Meat Mark mentioned, "It's about nine-twenty. If we hold out for forty more the War will be won."

What did he mean by; "Hold Out." We're Americans. We don't "Hold Out" and "Wait" to win. Hell No! We do what Teddy did; we charge.

How can you win by "Holding Out"? Isn't that the same as saying you don't want to play the game anymore. If we're going to "Hold Out"; why not just go on home and take a shower?

"Hold Out?" Name one American man in Nineteen Sixty-Eight that would think of such a thing? Shit; most of them hadn't a clue of what it even meant.

In less time than it took me to break five more projectiles I could see Meat was getting the attention of Mike. Mike then threw a dirt-bomb, hitting Wayne on the leg getting his attention.

Looked to me, then and there, that the "Hold Out" option was no longer being discussed. Far from it. Instantly Wayne scrambled to San Juan where he and Mike both came behind me.

They started pulling and cracking, as I was, and Mike made the plan known, "We'll pick up Bingo and follow your brother and Al over. You take San Juan. Don't want them thinking we're going right."

Mike was right about me taking over his hill. If I were to move to Cavanal they would surely suspect we were making a move. We had to make them think we were staying put on the front.

All this time Mark and Meat were breaking weeds, massing a stockpile to give the guys as they hid behind the barren hills. I was now on the front line, which changed my strategy to what we all did on the front. Only every other whomba was airborne; you had to start a pile for your advance.

Meat had stopped dead in his tracks and was pointing to Schultz.

He would look to his right and yell, "Look at Schultz." Then he'd look to his left and yell the same thing.

We all stopped and stared. It was unbelievable. I think even the other side stopped and stared.

Schultz was now covered from head to toe in green slime. Even his face had a somewhat green glow to it.

Gooch yelled over the confusion, "It's the Freakin Green Giant!"

I didn't know if it was true or not. Because the only thing that separated this green monster from the one that sold corn and baby peas was the ever-present, totally visible swastika on his forehead.

No shit! It was the only part of his body that wasn't green and dirty. I guess he kept wiping his forehead and eyes to get the crap out of them. Each time uncovering his recently acquired branding.

I heard an opponent's weed whiz by my ear and I immediately hit the dirt; literally. San Juan was dustier than where I had been due to all the movement around it.

Bunker Hill to my left was almost out of good weeds and Meat and Mark on my right were still getting half of their supply from the front of Capitol Hill. Mike was an experienced whombaer and didn't strip his hill down to bare bones. He even left quite a substantial canopy to hide under.

I was starting to wonder if we had at least crossed the halfway point when Meat yelled, "Fire!" He yelled it like he meant it.

Schultz was back to his five or six wet ones at a whack; dripping the whole time as they flew from point A to point B.

I moved a little to my left to get a better throwing range and came upon a small stockpile Mike had left behind. I winged those bastards off in less time than ever. I know it was a record for me; I just hoped it was good enough for them. I could see Bingo's ass as he scrambled to take the first enemy hill.

Keeping an eye on that hill furthest to our right, just over the enemy line, I could tell we had a few of ours now on their turf. I wasn't sure if they had all made it across. Mark hit me with a dirt bomb and made the thumbs up sign. This made me try even harder to give them greater air support.

Sal's guys were now pinned down to the middle and back hills. We could tell by the way the incoming was hitting they were mostly in the middle; maybe one or two in the back. I didn't feel the drops from Schultzie's whombas, so I turned around. He wasn't there; he was nowhere.

"Holy Shit!" I couldn't believe what the hell he was doing. He was pulling the biggest weeds from his neighboring hills; Big Round Top and Little Round Top. He was snapping about three or five at a time and putting them in the slime. When he had about a dozen he was running them up to Mark and Meat.

"Was the kid crazy like they all insisted?" was all I could think.

On his way back to the Matterhorn he stopped and ran toward me. Ducking under the superb canopy Mike had constructed he informed me that from his vantage point he didn't think there was anyone directly in front of Bunker Hill. He was sure they were concentrated on our right.

He could see that Al, Gooch, Mike and Bingo had all crossed. He now wanted to know if I'd join him on a run around the left side.

I told him I'd go, and he sped off toward Meat and Mark. After what seemed an hour he was back by my side. It took him a while longer this time because he stopped at Capitol Hill to fire about a dozen off at the enemy. Mark had told him he would take my place at San Juan and try to cover us. Seemed like a viable plan of attack.

I was cracking weeds when Schultz came back with the plan. He would be ready in about two minutes. First he wanted me to join him in soaking six whombas in the slime to take with us.

He was always thinking; of what though I'm not really sure. We left our projectiles in the scum while we figured out which was our best path. He decided we should both go to the hill in front of San Juan.

I agreed with his choice and told him Mike had left some rather large weeds on either side and in the front to serve as protection. Schultz just smiled. I knew that grin; he was going to throw each and every one of those damn weeds.

The way he kept turning and looking back at his hill, his moat, it finally hit me. The son-of-a-bitch was going to crack a bunch then fallback to soak them. I knew he was up to something.

I hit the right side of San Juan; dropping my stash as I took cover. He kept running and finally crawling made his way to Cemetery. He dropped all the slimy green whombas and ran back toward Little Round Top.

He pulled the last of the big ones and retreated to the moat. When he had that load wet and ready to go he hustled them up to Meat and Mark. He was back next to me in a flash.

"Ready!" was all he said. He didn't ask it; he said it.

He didn't even give me time to answer; he was gone. He was behind the hill waving me forward under the protection of an aerial assault; consisting of mostly green slimy whombas.

By the time I joined him he was pointing to our right. Gary had moved when we did; leaving Little Round Top falling in with Mark and Meat. Mark ran over to us and filled us in on what was happening on the right.

Al and Mike had jumped up to the second row on the hill to the very right. They knocked out Chad; so that made them six. Gooch, Wayne and Bingo were still at the hill just over the border and under heavy fire.

Next thing I knew Meat was sitting in the dirt next to me. He looked as serious as any officer under fire. He ordered us, "Mark; how about you stay here with Paulie. Schultz you come with me."

That was that. Mark stayed and Schultz followed. Meat went back toward Gary at Cemetery and Schultz went on his merry way. Oh sure; he was moving back to the rear, but he was happy.

Mark and I couldn't see behind us due to San Juan Hill, but we had our suspicions. We fired our whombas; as did all the rest.

Then we had a visit from Santa Schultz. He was back by us with a shitload of slime soaked whombas. He did a dump and run. Not even taking the time to grin or cuss. By the time we had thrown our allotment we could see them flying from where Gooch, Wayne and Bingo were.

Meat had left Gary at Cemetery and was making deliveries for his Schultz. Next thing I know Gary moves up between us and the others on our right. We now had the first row of the opponent's hills. It was only a matter of time before they'd surrender. Hell, I was ready to surrender and I was just throwing the stinking, green root-balls.

The whombas were flying full scale from our side, but not like it had been earlier from theirs. Neither Mark nor I noticed Al had crawled in beside us. He was out of breath and totally exhausted.

Al was puffing and trying to speak, "We've got the second row hill on the right. Great job. God Damn Schultzie is a one man ballistic missile silo. He doesn't stop. Just keeps cranking 'em.

Gooch, Wayne and Bingo are getting the swamp whombas from Schultzie and they're pummeling the bastards now. Think you can get that wipe on the far left. If you can, get word to me. Later."

Al was off and out of sight as mysteriously as he appeared. I told Mark to sit while I made a swamp run. I returned with four apiece; worried the entire time I was taking too long.

With our putrid whombas we made our move. Gary was aware of our destination and gave cover. Meat ran immediately to where we were. We could tell he was about to follow us in.

I threw one miss and Mark threw one. When the guy thought he had us and jumped out in the clear to fire one off Meat hit him square in the chest.

Mark and I didn't even look back. Hell no; we ran for cover. I can still see Mark diving head first into that hill. We expected to get clobbered the second we landed, but nothing. The hill just past it, to the left, was vacant. The others were pinned down from the fire of the rest of our side.

Mark and I waved Meat to come in to our hill. We had figured their side was down at least four. Meat made a dash for that third empty hill past ours and caught one in the back.

"Shit!" was all Marc and I heard.

Then we saw him stand and dust himself off; walking toward the houses. Gary heard the howl and relayed the bad news to his right.

# Chapter 14: Saturday 9:33 a.m.

Maybe it was that they were watching Meat leave the field or maybe they weren't paying attention. Either way; Mark took off to that third hill and made it.

This hill was virgin territory and Mark was cranking out whombas to beat all hell. Now we had two of their guys trapped in a crossfire. Actually it was more like they were the center of a triangle.

There was one guy on Mark's right firing a few his way, but he never responded. He kept on and on after the hill in front of me; to my right. He knew it was just a matter of time and one of them would get hit. They were starting to slow their firing back which gave me the impression they were running out of ammo. Gary took the decrease in the action as a time to run over to me.

He started laughing when I asked, "What the hell you doing here?"

He replied, "They stripped these hills bare, haven't you noticed. Where's Schultzie? I ran out. Is he ghosting?"

He was dead on about the conditions of their front row. Without our Schultzie bring ammo we had no choice but to move. When Mark threw a dirt-bomb my way, I took it as a signal to advance around the left; Gary came with me.

Thinking the way was clear we ran right up to where Mark was. He was screaming the whole time that there were still two guys on the hill to our right. We never saw them or anything resembling a whomba coming from the hill.

I could see Mark shrug his shoulders and Gary got a strange look on his face. He took his two whombas and two I had just cracked and started for that very hill. I thought he was nuts. But what the hell; I quickly broke two and followed. Yup, there were two guys behind that hill.

Gary shocked the crap out of them when he yelled, "Howdy Neighbor!"

I was laughing so hard I missed both my shots.

I guess it was luck that Gooch came to our rescue. Gary did manage to get one of them and Gooch got the other one. I scrambled around the north side of the hill and got two more weeds pulled. Now I had to concentrate on the guy right in front of me. There might have been only three left; you'd never know it by the amount they were sending into the air.

I stalled for a moment when I saw the backs of the two guys walking toward the houses. Sure enough; one of them was Sal. I thought their side should still be OK; in the fighting mood. After all, we just lost Meat and it didn't stop us. Then again, we still had nine guys to play the game on our side.

We were kids, what do kids know about the inevitability of a war. Sure the numbers alone assured me our side was going to win. But remember, Sal's guys were all Americans. Just as our side was all Americans.

We Americans don't let silly numbers cloud our judgment when there's a game involved. Proof is that Korean War game we had just played. It was something like twenty billion million trillion of theirs to a whopping three-hundred twenty-six thousand eight-hundred and sixty-three of ours. And that was at the peak in Nineteen Fifty-Three. We didn't think twice of not playing; we're Americans.

In the time that we were "fooling around" over on our side, it seemed the Army of Gantner had made a vital strategic advance. They managed to get the two hills on the far right to surrender.

Shit, I would have too. It was Al, Mike, Gooch, Wayne and Bingo all whombarmed to the hilt. At first they debated whether to give up or not. More than likely when they saw Schultzie on the hill coming their way; that was the clincher.

Craig, the last man on their team still in the game, surrendered as soon as he realized he was the only one left. This was the formal end of the game.

We could see Sal and the others walking back toward the hills from their shady spot. Each one of us on my side seemed to look no different than any of the guys on their side. We were all one group of dirty, smelly kids. I guess Schultz would actually be the MVP of stink; he was covered in that green stuff.

We all stood around dusting and spitting; trying to get a clean airway to our lungs. It would take us longer to get somewhat comfortable in our new skins of dirt, than the length of the game.

Once all the action had ceased you can't believe how much you itched and felt like crap. I mean the dirt was even in our socks and underwear; it was everywhere. Funny how we all knew we couldn't go home looking like this; even if we were "War" heroes.

Two guys on the other side told Schultz to stay at least ten feet away and downwind from us. This only made the rest of us laugh. He ignored them and had unfastened his belt to rearrange himself; enough said.

Then from out of the blue Schultzie yells, "Hey, my package looks like a fresh dug Idaho potato."

Mike yelled back to him, "Come on Schultzie; it ain't that big."

Schultz was tearing he was laughing so hard, "Maybe not; but it's just as dirty."

I'll never forget how Wayne just fell to the ground. He was howling to the point you could hear him wheezing trying to catch his breath. There wasn't one guy out of the whole twenty that wasn't pissing himself laughing.

One of Sal's guys made a comment, something to the effect, that if we didn't have Schultz we would have lost. I didn't agree out loud, but I could have. It sure would have been the truth. I guess they all knew it; cause we all did.

Here we stood after the first major war on the hills. The Whomba War of Sixty-Eight was over; without any need for a rematch or future confrontation. In less than an hour's time we had settled the argument that had pitted our side against theirs. The argument that couldn't be settled by conversation and diplomacy.

This only proved again to me that my father's generation is right when they preach, "Talk my ass. We'll play the bastards and beat them into the ground. We're Americans. We don't discuss nothing."

Yes, I certainly did agree at that time with the thinking of the Sixties. Why would any country use a diplomatic channel to work out a difference when a war, a game, was so much more fun?

I mean, you don't get heroes from a meeting. How could you? There's no dirt, no pain, no wounded and there wouldn't be any dead.

Who in their right mind would want to discuss anything? Maybe a girl. Maybe our mothers. Then again they're Americans; they'll want a game too.

My brother must have known of every swimming pool within eight hundred miles of our house. He made the announcement he was certain the McGhees were out of town on vacation and maybe we should all jump in their pool.

Gary agreed, "We were in it last night and the water is really warm."

So we were off; all twenty of us.

Hitting the river road I saw Mark looking at the back of Meat's shirt. He told Meat to stop and lifted it up toward his shoulders.

It was a tragic sight. Two inches below the shoulder blade was a gash about three inches long and a piece of root sticking out.

Meat hadn't made any mention of his back hurting; that was until Mark touched his shirt. Gooch took a look and told Meat he may need stitches.

The troops came to a halt under the parkway bridge and we inspect ourselves and each other for wounds, both minor and major. I had what appeared to be a piece of dirt or stone under my skin just below my knee; must have gotten it from crawling.

Al still had so much dirt in his nose he had to breathe through his mouth. Bingo was complaining he couldn't hear out of his left ear. Turns out the whomba broke apart on the hill inches from his head. My brother thought the sticky stuff on his left ankle was scum from the moat. It wasn't; scum is green, not red.

My mother was a nurse and I can say with the medical knowledge I knew at the time that every one of these wounds was a nightmare. Even the smallest scratch was a disaster to someone working in an emergency room.

From the smallest cut to the largest laceration, all had one thing in common. They were made by a pointed object covered with dirt. Even if the root didn't go in the dirt certainly did. If there was a break in the skin it was filled with dirt.

As if the dirt and roots and pieces of shit weren't bad enough; the other side had to deal with the green slime. Only God could even guess what the hell that shit was composed of. And I would even bet he hadn't a clue.

The other side was bitching about getting that shit in their eyes, ears and mouths. We did have our little Geneva Convention some hours after The War. All types of slime and puddle water were no longer acceptable under the convention; little good it did Sal's team.

From what I gathered, standing under that bridge, not one of us escaped without a mark. Of course Schultz came into the battle with the worst mark and would leave with it as well.

Al brought up the idea maybe we should skip the pool and head to our homes to get clean. It was voted upon and we said our goodbyes and headed back. We walked the path along the parkway trying to stay out of sight from all our neighbors. We did look like shit; no exception.

Wayne and Mark took forever to hop the fence back into their yard. We could hear Wayne moaning the entire time and Mark yelling for him to hurry the hell over.

My brother was asking Meat what the true reason for The War was and he told him to ask Al.

When Al started explaining with a one word answer I knew we were in trouble, "Girls."

Gooch asked, "Which girls?"

Al grinned out, "You know those two over by the lake. The knockout with the blond hair and her cousin. The ones from over by St. Stans."

I remember my brother giving Al a few choice words of advice, "If you plan on dragging my ass into another Whomba over two stuck-up bitches like that. Well, just don't ask. Christ's sake Al, those two?"

Mike turned around getting ready to make a comment and Gary cut him off, "We fought for the Polish Belles; the looker twins? Don't say another word. Don't."

Mike had to ask, "You mean the ones we saw over at Januk's a couple of weeks ago?"

Gary jumped ugly before Al could say anything, "Yeah. Marilyn Monroe and her cousin; God's-gift-to-men. Remember that dark haired one? God Al. How could you?"

Mike started to laugh; he had good reason. He had a girl, a steady girl. He didn't worry about all the shit like the others did. He didn't have to fight for the one he was after; not now anyway.

But he was just like every one of us on our street. When one got in a fix, the others were in the same fix. Funny how he was fighting for something he'd never get the benefit of. Kind of like what Vietnam was all about. Our guys were dying for something that would never and could never benefit them or the United States of America.

We slowly ambled up the grass embankment toward the bridge and our homes. I could tell by the overbearing silence that maybe, just maybe, the older guys had a feeling they had bit off more than they could chew.

It didn't take a nuclear scientists or a brain surgeon to see we were all in bad shape; and we had won. Well, according to the rules of war we had won. Looking at Meat's back I was now having my doubts.

Lagging behind the other seven; I couldn't help thinking our "War" could have been avoided and settled in a more civilized way.

We could have had a dart match at Januk's or maybe a game of tackle football. Though, I had to agree it was quite invigorating; more so than a game of darts could ever be.

So, all-in-all, I guess the older guys were right. I'm only fourteen; who am I to question my superiors? Isn't this how the true soldier does his job? He never questions the authority of his smarter, more intelligent higher-ups.

I wanted to ask Al one question, but we were about to hop the fence. I wanted to know if our "War" was really a deliberate result of what he and Meat had done with those foreign, insignificant girls or was it more of an excuse to have a full-blown engagement.

I was totally aware that the American way of handling a disagreement in the Sixties, as in years before, was to strike any enemy who was confrontational.

Seeing this attitude extend to our street, our neighborhood, could only instill pride in the American public. The intelligence of our adolescent leaders brought out the patriotic duties of all involved to protect and defend the homeland.

I know I wasn't alone in wondering just what and who we were protecting the neighborhood from. Now I can honestly say I do understand completely what the guys coming back from Nam are talking about.

They were saying the same things I was saying today for the past thirteen years, "What the hell are we doing over there? What have they ever done to us? We bomb and shoot these people for what reason? Run that by me again?"

I was the last over the fence because I steadied it so Meat could get over without it swaying. Still in my own world, walking behind the rest, I really wanted to know the answers; the reasons.

Am I that different from the other nine in wanting to know. "Why?"

Am I being un-American, unpatriotic, when I question why we fight and beat up our neighbor? The same neighbor we're going to meet at the bar tonight. That is; if everyone can manage to walk and carry their battered bodies over there.

# Chapter 15: Saturday Afternoon

Parked on my bed the time didn't seem to pass at all. I could hear the sound of the shower and couldn't remember if my brother were in there ten seconds or ten minutes.

I was so scared to move and get more dirt all over the place than we had already put down. I caught myself praying to God to get him out, so I could get this dirt encrusted shell off of me. Finally; the sound of running water suddenly stopped.

He ran from the bathroom into the bedroom to tell me my turn was up. He had the look of wanting to tell me something more, something vital; you know how brothers can read each other. But he was well aware it would have to wait until I was back.

My need for a wash-down was far more important at this juncture than whatever information he had to share. Anyway; The War was over. It was time to chill.

I scrubbed myself as hard, if not harder, than what I would do to remove scales from a largemouth bass. My skin was sore from my head down.

I wasn't bothered that much by the bruise below my knee before I started the cleaning, but as soon as I touched it the blood just wouldn't stop. It didn't hurt all that much; it just worried me more and more. I stepped onto the rug trying to think of a way not to leave the bathroom resembling a slaughterhouse.

Drying off with my left hand, I held a wad of toilet paper on my shin with the right. Talk about annoying. I must have used half a roll trying to towel-off and get my underwear on. Still holding the paper on my shin I ran back to my room.

My brother was sitting waiting for me with a box of tissues next to him on the bed. He too had a wad of paper pressed hard against a part of his anatomy. He removed it for a second; just long enough for me to see a good one inch gash along his ankle. It looked bad. I thought mine was bad; it was nothing compared to his.

He had put the volume up a little more than usual on the radio thinking it would shield our voices from our mother's ears. It may have done a grand job at that, but it had no affect what-so-ever on our hemorrhaging.

I went to the closet to retrieve cotton wadding, bandages and tape. With two boys and one grown man in the house, the array of first-aid essentials was endless. He chose the cotton and tape; looked to me one roll wasn't going to cut it.

Back from another trip to the box of bandages, I couldn't help noticing the huge red packing in the waste can. He had used the entire box and it acted more like a wick than a covering.

His face showed me more than the disgusted appearance of a brother who couldn't stop the flow of blood no matter how hard he pressed down. It was now starting to show the telltale signs of pain. We both were well aware that the more the infection spread, the more it would swell and hurt.

I don't remember which one of us was the first to throw in the towel, but it was time to show our newly achieved awards to our dear mother. This was nothing new in our household; emergency room trips were at least a once a year occurrence. Though this may set the record of two going at the same time. So much for grin and bear it; we both knew it would only get worse.

One inspection by our mother, the register nurse, and the verdict was read. We were both going for a ride. She really didn't yell all that much, for a change; it was more of a formal inquisition.

She simply asked, "How did you both manage to get cut? Where were you? Was it clean?"

My brother led the way saying we were at the ball field. Sitting in the backseat I was trying to avoid looking into the rearview mirror. I may have been younger, but I would have come up with something better than that.

I mean, after all these years, "At the ball field?"

The ride to Hackensack went smother than the time I slit my finger with the carrot slicer or got my foot smashed while seeding the field on the tractor. Maybe it was because we both were injured, and our Mom thought she could get us to breakdown with the silent treatment.

I was running a Hendrix song in my head when my brother said something I knew couldn't be true. Or could it? He started jabbering about getting his ankle cut by a stick.

Yeah; it was over. By the time we hit the entrance doors of the ER she knew the entire story. Not about The War; just about us fooling around down by the river and throwing "Stuff" at each other. She didn't have time to say anything as a response, because she was greeted by everyone at the hospital.

She had gone to school and worked there for years. Every doctor, nurse, orderly, housekeeper and security guard made sure they said their "hellos" and moved us swiftly toward our destination. It wasn't like they needed to guide us. My mother had worked there over ten years and I had made at least seven trips for various injuries; that I could remember.

Uncle Bill, a male nurse we've known since birth, pointed to a room on the right; my brother and I took our seats while our mother remained outside talking to her nurse friends.

I was accustomed to the routine and started taking my bandages off. My brother was still afraid his would bleed out like a stuck pig.

Time flew by and we were on our way. It was always nice to visit the ER and see all our friends. My leg was cleaned, disinfected and bandaged; that was quick. I was given an erythromycin tablet to take right away and a prescription to get filled on the way home. My brother's wound seemed to take forever.

I bet it took a good thirty minutes for them to clean his ankle and put the eight stitches in. First they talked about an X-Ray, then they decided against it. He told the doctor he had been walking fine all morning; just some pain. They gave him Tylenol#3s and the same antibiotic I was given. That was that; we were good to go.

The way out was as slow, if not slower, than the way in. Everyone kept asking when they'd see us again.

My mother wasn't laughing when one doctor laughed, "Try not to stay away so long next time."

I looked out toward the parking lot through the two sets of double doors. Thinking, "Shit! That doctor may have been on to something."

I know I thought that first, just before I thought, "I hope to hell they don't talk to Mom."

The "They" I was referring to was Meat with his father. Mrs. Winters took one look at him when he got home and wouldn't even let him take a shower. She called her husband at work and had him come right home. He brought him right over to the hospital.

Meat said later on, as he showed us his back, that his father told my mother, "Looks like the boys had a fun morning."

We knew Meat. He didn't talk about The War. Even if he did to his father, that wouldn't have mattered. His father knew the entire lowdown on us kids and never, ever told anyone. He was such a great man; you could trust him with anything.

My brother was rubbernecking real hard at this Cadillac as we pulled out of the parking lot.

When I realized why, all I could think of was, "Man, I hope Mom doesn't see them."

I know my brother was thinking the same thing. It was Mrs. Boniface and Bingo. I figured it must have been his ear. When he left us at our house he still couldn't hear out of that one side.

I wasn't worried the whole time we rode over here, but now I was starting to get scared. Four out of ten in less than an hour. We may be running into more of our friends with wounds before we made it safely home.

Upon entering the house, after a nerve-wracking ride home, my brother grabbed the phone and called over to the Rileys. Gary answered the phone and acted like everything was normal on his end of the line.

He wasn't at all shocked to hear how we had spent the latter part of the morning and part of the afternoon. Gary told my brother Al was in the shower almost half an hour before he finally started getting his nose unclogged. He even laughed about how his brother sounded like a cartoon character with all the dirt up his nose.

The two Garys decided to meet over at the ball field in an hour; even though playing was out of the question. Word was being passed to the Winters and D'Amicos by Gary; my brother was to call Schultzie and Bingo.

I was telling my brother I had my doubts about Meat being in form to show up; just then the phone rang. Gooch answered and mouthed the word "Meat". After a minute he hung up and informed me he'd be there.

He also told my brother he'd be walking. His back hurt too much to drive.

Gooch, Gary, Al and myself made it to the bench around four. It wasn't more than twenty minutes and the rest of the squad gathered around.

Wayne was walking so slow and strange that Schultz asked him if he had shit his pants. When he was within a

couple of feet of all of us he lifted his pant leg as far as the
brace would allow.

His mother had taken him over to Saddle Brook Hospital
for a torn ligament. He wasn't supposed to be walking or
even out of the house. When his parents went shopping at
Paramus Mall, he and Mark left.

First thing Meat asked Bingo when he walked up was did
he talk to Sal. All Bingo could do was shake his head and try
not to laugh.

"Did I talk to Sal? Yeah, I talked to Sal."

After sitting down on the pavement next to the bench he
looked toward Wayne as if asking for a joint.

Wayne got the message and Bingo continued with his
answer, "Looks like Fred won't be going to the bar tonight.
Both his eyes are bandaged. Sal said he got a whomba right
in the face. Both got a shit-load of dirt in them and one got
piece of a root. Eye doctor worked on him for about two
hours. He's got to go back tomorrow; on Sunday no less."

Meat could only say what the rest of us were thinking,
"That sucks. Anymore peanuts?"

Bingo assured us they took a lot more suffering than we
did; and a few of theirs were quite serious.

I tried not to think the thoughts that wanted to cloud my
mind.

The thoughts that seemed to want to ask the questions, "It
was a game. How do we get major wounds in a game?
Wasn't this morning supposed to be fun? We don't hate each
other; we're all Americans. How can one American kid do so
much harm to another American kid? Hell, it's not right. It's
not patriotic at all."

Bingo went on, after a small break for an inhale, "It's still on for tonight; over at Januk's. So if you guys want we should head over around eight. I'm thinking of walking, so I guess I'll leave around seven-thirty."

Meat spoke right up, "I can't drive with my back. I'm with you."

Looking around he saw everyone else nod in agreement to the time. Even I was nodding. It would be very crowded tonight and even I should have no problem getting at least two.

My brother stood looking as if he was making ready to go back home. He looked around at all the troops and informed us he needed another pain pill. I was getting hungry and decided to go also.

The rest all stood within seconds and the slow weary troop meandered toward the bridge. Wayne kept complaining we were moving too fast. His brother kept reminding him if he wanted to go tonight he better shut up or start toward the bar now.

The Rileys went into their house and the rest of us turned left to start walking home. As the D'Amicos were about to turn right Schultz yelled to Wayne he'd better keep going south if he wanted to get a beer before closing time. Of course we all laughed. Why wouldn't we?

We always made jokes about the wars; the wounded, the killed and the dead and buried. We were all Americans after all. Isn't that what we do? We go to war. We fight the war.

And if you're lucky enough to get home in what resembles one piece; you discuss, brag and joke about the war.

My brother hurried in for a pill, while I took advantage of the time alone to sit on the steps for a few minutes and think. This small war of ours. This very, very short act of aggression; if it could even be called that was certainly questionable.

I mean all the wars I had studied in school lasted months; if not tens of years. Here in less than an hour the two sides battled and finished it; for once and for all. Is this a true war?

If the Whomba War could be fought and resolved in the time between breakfast and lunch, why couldn't The Other War our country was waging?

I mean, we had a whopping total of twenty lives to play with; out government has endless. We set a time limit and a limit on what kind of weapons were justifiable and legal. Why can't the greatest Democracy every to walk the planet do the same? After all, they surely have more resources than we have.

Shit, after five minutes I would have been happy if the game ended. We planned on playing an hour and it didn't even last that long. I can't imagine a game going on for a full day; or even a full ten years.

Al told me the politicians really like playing these games. Well; he must be right on that. They play what seems forever.

I can't imagine how the young men actually in the game handle it day-in and day-out. No wonder we have the National Lottery. I'm only fourteen and I wouldn't want to play for more than an hour; let alone six months.

# Chapter 16: Saturday Night, Party Night

I couldn't help but smile as I noticed that dumb smirk on Al's face as we entered the bar. The front room was packed with all the usual residents and his vision immediately focused on the clock on the wall with the Clydesdales. He was right again. It wasn't even eight-thirty yet and the place was standing room only.

He hit my leg, giving me the signal, he'd grab us each one while I headed straight back to the tables. His motto concerning me was always, "Out of sight. Out of mind."

The two tables in the back remained hidden from view as the armies from both sides stood around drinking and telling stories. I did a quick headcount and could make an educated guess that there were seventeen of us. I was eager to learn who and why the other two hadn't shown; I already knew about Fred.

Speaking of Fred, Al was tapping my shoulder asking me to join him out by the bar. Fred's grandfather had been talking to him for a few minutes and wanted to talk some more. I took a long hard drink and put my fresh beer down on the table by the wall.

Al and I stood next to Mr. Uski, who was at the bar with his comrades, trying not to let my age impede with our socializing. My grandfather had known this man his entire life. He was what we kid's called, "One of us."

The wide grin on his face was only surpassed by the men to either side of him. I could have dropped right then and there when he put a beer in front of me and said, "I guess the older brats stole yours when you went in the pool room."

Al was trying not to laugh or look directly at Januk, who was tending bar. It was obvious to me he had to know that one of the newly pulled foam-topped icy mugs was for me. After all; there were more mugs than people at our end of the bar.

Al was Al. He stood there with that shit-eating grin the whole time. He'd even chuckle each time I raised my pint for a drink.

All of us kids, both from our town and the town we were in, had heard the scoop about most of the older men in the bar by the time we were five years old. We'd hear the stories from our grandparents, our parents, our neighbors and our friends. If you were actually lucky enough; sometimes you'd hear the stories directly from them.

They all didn't mind having Al around. They'd even make him sit with them sometimes and they'd buy his drinks.

My grandfather told me Mr. Uski loved the way Al would have three beers and then start asking questions. Questions that Mr. Uski and his armed forces buddies thought were honest and relevant.

Fred's grandfather took a sip and while looking down at Al, over the end of his pint, asked; "OK soldiers, how'd your side fare? Better than ours I hope."

I was well aware that he had put an "s" on the word soldier. Al was older; shouldn't he be doing all the explaining? I should have seen it coming.

One, he just bought my beer and two, he was friends with my grandfather.

I was thinking, trying to avoid direct eye contact, "I bet my grandfather called you. Or did you call him?"

He spoke right up, "So Paulie. Your grandfather called me."

Had I said anything aloud? Did they hear what I was thinking?

Al was giving me the "Stare". You know; the "What the hell are we gonna do now?" kind of stare.

He waited until one of his friends returned from the bathroom and then continued on with his investigation. We could tell by now that most likely all the men in the bar had heard some version of the situation.

Obviously not enough though. Or was it they were so accustomed and used to each other's war stories they wanted to hear a new one; a fresh one. Couldn't be any fresher than a war that happened only ten hours ago.

Al had to be thinking what I was thinking, "Why don't you go in the poolroom and ask them? Half of them in there are your relatives and neighbors. Why you bothering me? Us?"

All my self-mental interrogation must have appeared like silence from a deaf mute, cause Al took it as his cue to take over.

He had so many conversations about the Second World War and the Korean War with these guys he was actually happy to have A War of his own to relay to them.

Now the shoe was on the other foot. It was the old men asking the questions about "our" War. He was now the soldier in the story; in our War story.

Growing up in the Sixties, one thing that was a certain fact was that when the old guys would ask a kid a question; they expect an honest answer.

We may have left out some details and names, so as not to get ourselves or others in deep shit; but most of the time we confessed. Besides; a lot of my friends growing up were Catholic. They always swore Confession was good for one's soul.

I was facing Mr. Cohen when Januk put a pitcher down in front of Al and didn't move.

He saw the expression on Al's face change instantly and responded with, "I want to hear this too. Go ahead. Hey Paulie, don't be shy, put your glass over here."

I did what I was told, and he filled my pint to the top.

Pulling the glass back my way he laughed at me so loud all of the guys could hear, "Don't tell your father."

There was no way that was going to happen. This was the first and probably the last time he'd ever give me a beer. I could tell his generosity had but one motive. Make the boys happy and make the boys talk.

The poolroom might have been echoing with the adolescent noise. This main room was as quiet as a chapel as the gray-hairs tuned in to hear the latest account of this morning's War.

Al was saying a few words, then stopped dead in his tracks. He looked Januk in the eyes. Then turning to Mr. Uski said, "Please excuse me a second."

I thought, and so did everyone else I think, that he was going to the bathroom.

He stuck his head in the poolroom and yelled, "Can you guys come out here for a minute?"

I could have shit. Here we go again; another Al deal.

The guys were backing against the walls and tables trying to all squeeze in the room. I was panicking to look around at each table; to see if all the inhabitants would be "cool" with what was about to go down.

Suddenly I felt Ok with what he was about to do. All these men, each and every one, were a veteran of a war. Each one had been through the worst and lived to tell about it. They had shared their nightmares with us all these years. Why shouldn't we share our measly conflict with them?

Al, along with Meat and Sal at his side, told our story. The three combatants started at the beginning and talked for about twenty minutes explaining everything right up until the very end. Even the hospital trips.

Meat even went into detail about his back and the trip he made with his father. Sal gave a play by play accounting of how his men tried to invade the enemy hills, only to be repelled at a high cost.

I was finally enlightened as to what happened to the other two guys missing from tonight's post-war celebration.

Billy O'Rourke had gotten a large sliver of glass in his knee and couldn't walk. The hospital had given him crutches, but his parents wouldn't let him out of the house.

Peter Fox didn't get hurt all that bad. His father just went ballistic when he heard about what we had done and put him under house-arrest.

This seemed a little strange to me. Why would you incarcerate your own child for being in a game? He was an American too. We're supposed to play war; aren't we?

All the top television shows and movies have "war" as their main theme. We're just doing what comes natural to a kid in Nineteen Sixty-Eight. His parents should be proud of him for enlisting into a war on his own. I'm certain our government would be.

The faces of the men hearing our news for the first time were indescribable. They were mesmerized; almost comatose. They held the same facial expressions that I or any of us kids would have when told about the Battles of Wake or the Bulge.

Not one glass was raised for a swallow during this entire time frame; except by the soldiers less than eighteen years of age.

Was I alone in seeing what they were feeling? It wasn't an expression of awe or enthusiasm. Far from it. It was definitely an appearance, an outward manifestation of disbelief; if not horror.

I could see on those faces the same look they must have had some time back when they were in the foxholes or life-rafts; clinging to any hope of life. It was the same mask worn by the older men as they told us about the mustard gas attacks in the trenches.

We had unknowingly turned a joyful evening at the neighborhood pub into a sullen wake for the survivors of War; all of this in less than thirty minutes.

The band of brothers I was so closely attached to and the enemy I tried to destroy this morning all blended into one small harmonious crowd. It was impossible to differentiate who was on whose side. There was no dividing line here in the bar; there was no us or them.

The low rumble of our voices was interrupted by Mr. Cohen asking, "So will you lads mind showing me a raised hand if you think your War this morning was the best way to settle this disagreement?"

I held my hand down waiting for the others to respond to Mr. Cohen's simple request. I'm sure they weren't waiting for me to go first; I was the youngest of the entire lot.

Looking from wall to wall, from face to face, all I saw were the other participants of the game doing exactly the same thing. After all the bragging and the joking and the winning; still no hands flying high?

I couldn't raise my hand. I was brought up better than to tell a falsehood or more aptly; a big fat total lie. Just the fact that I alone was on antibiotics was enough for me to rethink our conflict and admit maybe we should have settled instead for a dart match.

I didn't think I was alone in the opinion that maybe Fred and Meat would have also liked it if our competition had a little less intensity, violence and dirt.

Mr. Cohen took a few sips out of his glass and now having the full attention of the bar made a simple statement in an almost whispering voice, "I see you boys have put up the same amount of hands in response to the same question my squad was asked the day we hit the beach in Normandy."

Looking around at all the other older men still silent in the room he added, "The GAME isn't as much fun as you're led to believe it will be, is it?"

The older Mr. Stiles was sitting at a table in the corner when he directed his question at Schultz. "And you Frankie. What the hell were you thinking? You trying to add to that dashing scar you won last month? You of all of them should know better. What the Hell is wrong with you kids today?"

He could have had a point, but he had to have known and understood that we were all Americans. We were all born here; right down the street for God's sake.

Our parents met during a War, dated during a War and most of us were conceived during a War. War is our heritage; it's as natural to us as the floating trash making its way to the mighty ocean on the wings of the ever-flowing Passaic.

These men, that now stood in judgment of us and our War, couldn't have thought like this when they were our age. They all went off to battle for love of country.

It surely can't matter that much if our country was actually attacked; can it? Is it possible for someone to be awarded the highest medals for bravery and then fifty or sixty years later reverse their views on the glory of war? Or is it they're not changing their stance at all?

Could it be they never bought into the whole "Game" thing to begin with? Could they all have been no different than us here now? It is possible that these older and wiser men, that we kids have known since birth, weren't all that stupid when they were twelve and fourteen? Has being an American really changed that much in the last seventy years?

These heroes of the last great Wars lived in a time most of us can't even comprehend. They were indoctrinated in the motto of God, Country and Mom's apple pie. They were raised by their parents, teachers, and religious leaders to be fine young upstanding men; willing and able to fight for their country. Any one of them having an independent opinion on the subject would be labeled a coward; today's label would be a Commie.

It dawned on me as I inspected each and every face around me that we were all Americans. Yes, even with our generational differences we were all the same.

These men prayed to the same God today that they prayed to over fifty years ago. The difference is back then they prayed for God to save their own asses; today they pray for God to save ours.

They know something we are either too young or too stupid to understand. War is a Game; a Game where both sides lose.

Januk put eleven pitchers on the bar and announced it was on him.

He waited for the initial run on the trough to subside; then turning to Al asked in a quiet voice if our War was rightly known as the "Rumba War".

I assumed he said it so softly because he thought he was mispronouncing it. He told us he had heard the word spoken a few times earlier in the evening over by the pool tables and knew it was some sort of tropical dance.

Al took the initiative to explain to Januk what our weapon of choice was. He gave him a quick rundown of the rules and the terrain.

I remember him asking, "So you kids played war by throwing sticks at each other? What the hell? Are you crazy or smoking that dope stuff?"

I noticed how careful Al was to never use the word "Whomba" in his descriptive tale. It was a code of ours; a secret known only to the warriors of the battle.

Sure, the words "Whomba War" would be uttered by us; though in mostly private conversations. We were now as guilty as other war veterans; censoring what the public needed and didn't need to know.

I really wanted to enlighten this old codger with the truth but knew I couldn't. I ran the words through my mind, "We're Americans! That's what we American kids do. We play war. We throw stuff at each other; snowballs, dirt-bombs and big ass weed roots."

If I thought he'd understand, I'd explain that we make weapons out of everything. Just like in the movies.

Looking over at Meat I could tell his back was starting to bother him again. I told him I was getting ready to go if he wanted to walk back when I did.

He told me Januk had let him use the phone to call his dad; he was on the way. Offering me a ride home; I took it.

Listening to the radio as I lie in bed I wasn't sorry at all I left the bar so soon. I was exhausted from all the day's activities. I could tell the following morning was going to be a bad one. My muscles were starting to tense up now, they'd be rock hard by midnight.

All the uneasiness I had leading up to Our War seemed to have vanished. Sleep would come faster tonight than the previous four nights.

The rock station was playing another one of those anti-war songs. Strange thing going round and round in my head at that time was maybe songs like these will catch on in a couple of years. There surely had to be other fourteen year-olds in the United States that played war every day and were starting to wonder why?

Still I knew; these other American kids like myself, thought war was our national right. It had to be what our country stood for. If not; why was it promoted more than getting a polio vaccine?

Living in these United States guaranteed that even an eight year-old would have the opportunity to play the greatest game ever invented. Where else can a kid use his

Christmas money to buy a plastic bazooka or a Winchester that shoots real BBs?

Sure, there were other things such as baseballs and board-games to play with but come on now. Nothing has ever been more fun than a good game of war. Is there anything that compares? It's better than everything else that's out there.

Well, maybe not better than everything. I would rather have Fred get his sight back, or Meat not be in so much pain. Come to think of it; maybe war isn't the best game to play. Even if all the politicians are telling us it is.

The older I get the more I don't know who to trust or believe. I mean the television is telling us every second that smoking cigarettes is great and safe; next thing you know they'll be saying that's a lie too.

I must not have turned the timer on the radio all the way to the right, because it just clicked off. That's OK; I really don't mind the quiet after a day like today. And now when I think of it; it was a day from Hell.

I'm going to be honest with myself and admit that my view on going off to fight in Nam hasn't changed. Especially after how I spent the hours from nine to noon this morning. I wouldn't play another game on those hills if you paid me a million dollars.

I couldn't be more explicit if I said, "You'd have to march me out by bayonet point." Guess that's why we have the draft.

Sure, I'm like every other American kid on my street; we love playing games. I'm thinking though after what we played this morning the game of "War" is something we might want to rethink.

Every kid over the age of seventeen in America can't be wrong when they ask us younger guys, "Why in the world would you want to play that?"

We never took the time to answer their stupid questions about playing war. What would they know anyway? Sure; I guess they're older. They might be a little more knowledgeable about it; maybe?

Though if they were; why the hell are they all sticking around waiting to get netted by Uncle Sam and shipped over to Asia?

Is it that big of a deal; being American? Is it worth getting killed over? I'm not sure anymore. I'm certain all twenty of us found out today it's not worth getting whombaed over.

I feel into a deep sleep wondering what it would be like to grow up in a land called America where every man, at every age, didn't have his own personal war.

Where old veterans could shut their eyes at night; without the help of drink after drink.

Where middle-aged veterans didn't have restless dream; after restless dream.

Where young veterans-in-the-wings could hit the pillow without hitting the drugs first.

Where a child like myself didn't stare at the ceiling wondering if a friend might be blinded for life from a secret conflict; only known to a select few as the "Whomba War".